Independent Living and Community Participation

Katherine O. Synatschk

Gary M. Clark ■ James R. Patton

D1591637

pro·ed
An International Publisher

8700 Shoal Creek Boulevard ■ Austin, Texas 78757-6897 ■ 800/897-3202 ■ Fax 800/397-7633 ■ www.proedinc.com

© 2008 by PRO-ED, Inc.
8700 Shoal Creek Boulevard
Austin, Texas 78757-6897
800/897-3202   Fax 800/397-7633
www.proedinc.com

ISBN-13: 978-1-4164-0336-4
ISBN-10: 1-4164-0336-1

Printed in the United States of America

2   3   4   5   6   7   8   9   10   11   10   09

Contents

Introduction

Today, society supports the successful transition from school to the adult world for students. As educators and others in the helping professions, we expect our students and clients to become participating members of the community. This goal applies to all students in our schools, including those with disabilities.

Legislative Mandates for Transition

Significant legislation has been passed to address the transition needs of students receiving special education services. Congress recently updated the nation's special education law, the Individuals with Disabilities Education Improvement Act of 2004 (IDEA, 2004), and sought to improve postsecondary results for students with disabilities by requiring public high schools to provide better transition planning.

Congress stated that providing effective transition services to promote successful postschool education or employment is an important measure of a school's accountability for the postsecondary performance of its students. The provisions mandated that the Individualized Education Program (IEP) team must consider all identified students who will reach the age of 16 for the next IEP and identify each student's transition strengths, needs, preferences, and interests in relation to the postsecondary outcome goals of education and training, employment, and independent living. However, many transition experts and advocates feel that age 16 is too late to start transition planning. IDEA 2004's federal regulations make it clear that IEP teams are free to begin transition planning at an earlier age if the team determines it appropriate to do so. Many students with learning disabilities can benefit from transition planning activities that begin in middle school.

New phrases, such as "results-oriented process," "focusing on improving the academic and functional achievement of the child (300.42(a)(1)), and "appropriate measurable postsecondary goals based upon age-appropriate transition assessments related to training, education, employment, and, where appropriate, independent living skills" are specific enough to leave little doubt as to Congress's intent for schools. While there is some flexibility in determining "appropriate" measurable postsecondary goals, "age-appropriate transition assessments," and the individual appropriateness of assessing independent living skills, the language of IDEA 2004 and its regulations mandate a transition assessment process. The nature of that process is also guided by legislative language with the phrases "based on the individual child's needs, taking into account the child's strengths, preferences, and interests" (300.42(a)(2)); and, of course, data for schools to provide a graduating or exiting student due to aging out "a summary of the child's academic and functional performance" (300.305(e)(3)).

The IDEA 2004 mandate for considering transition service needs for every student with a disability who is eligible for special services, beginning no later than the age 16 IEP, has the logical (and legal) consequences of directing schools to extend their academic assessment procedures to new kinds of ability and achievement performance outcome areas (e.g., self-determination, social skills, life skills, employability) and levels of strengths, preferences, and interests across all outcome areas (e.g., strengths, preferences, and interests related to postsecondary education, occupations, self-determination, interpersonal relationships, etc.).

The IDEA 2004 assessment requirements clearly state that present level of performance (PLOP) must include both *academic* and *functional* performance. It is the latter area that is causing the most concern for professionals who have left the teaching of functional knowledge and skills to parents and other teachers or professionals (Clark, in press).

Functional Outcomes

The professional literature related to the functional outcomes for individuals with disabilities once they leave school (i.e., adult outcomes) has focused for some time on three general areas: independent living, personal–social adjustment, and occupational adjustment (Cronin & Patton, 1993; Halpern, 1985; Kokaska & Brolin, 1985; Sitlington & Clark, 2005). Sitlington and Clark elaborated on these three areas, dividing them into nine major transition planning areas: communication and academic performance, self-determination, interpersonal relationships, integrated community participation, health and fitness, independent/interdependent daily living, leisure and recreation, employment, and further education and training. Describing a specific array of skills associated with the transition process gives direction to assessment for all students with disabilities (Clark, in press).

Sitlington, Neubert, Begun, Lombard, and Leconte (2007) provide the following working definition highlighting the essential elements of assessment for transition planning:

> Transition assessment is an ongoing process of collecting information on the student's strengths, needs, preferences, and interests as they relate to the demands of current and future living, learning, and working environments. This process should begin in middle school and continue until the student graduates or exits high school. Information from this process should be used to drive the IEP and transition planning process and to develop the Summary of Performance document detailing the student's academic and functional performance and post-secondary goals. (Sitlington et al., 2007, pp. 2–3)

Current practice in transition assessment includes a variety of approaches. Most state guidelines and professional literature (cf. Clark, 2007; Miller, Lombard, & Corbey, 2007; Sitlington et al., 2007) addressing assessment for transition planning under the new IDEA 2004 requirements suggest that assessment for transition services include tests, interviews, direct observation, and curriculum-based assessment. Using these approaches involves the use of both formal and informal procedures.

The *informal* transition assessment approach particularly lends itself to using assessment information for counseling and guidance concurrently with the assessment and instruction process. Teachers using specific surveys or checklists in instruction can provide individual or group guidance, based on the information students share. Parents can follow up on ideas that were expressed at school, and teachers can do the same for ideas that were expressed at home. School counselors, teachers, parents, and students can all participate in exploring ideas that emerge from informal transition assessments.

Ideally, schools will seriously and systematically address transition assessment and planning well before the student's sixteenth birthday, perhaps as early as middle school. Early assessment and planning for transition is important. For most students, with the goal of independence comes the need for skill development. Identifying and developing the skills needed in the areas of self-advocacy and self-determination, interpersonal skills, daily living, transportation and mobility, leisure, and community participation facilitates the development of a very relevant and functional curriculum. The motivation to achieve is enhanced when students learn skills that lead to their independence. Early awareness of transition needs helps students and their parents perceive that students have the abilities to be independent citizens of the community. By engaging in early transition assessment and planning, professionals can enhance the number and variety of options that are available to individual students, because there is additional time to provide the foundation needed to access those options.

It is our intention to provide age-appropriate informal transition assessments addressing independent living skills. We hope that the assessment tools in this book are useful for teachers, counselors, special educators, and others and expect that the instruments can be implemented in a wide variety of settings and delivery models. Some users are likely to have minimal time allocated for transition programming; others will have group sessions, class periods, or entire courses in which to work with students. Table 1 illustrates some of the delivery models frequently used.

Whether you have a few minutes a week for an individual session or a semester- or year-long course dedicated to transition, the informal assessments offered here can be used to involve your students systematically in a transition plan. In addition, within each section of the informal assessments, we have included multiple offerings on the same topic, designed to range from simple to complex to facilitate your selection of age-appropriate assessments. Informal assessments that are designed for students to complete as well as those designed to solicit teacher and parent input about the student's strengths, abilities, knowledge, preferences, interests, and progress are included. We provide these assessments and the ideas about delivery models to illustrate the variety of tools and settings available for use to address the transition needs of all students. Professionals will, of course, use their judgment to select the settings and methods most appropriate for students' life skills needs.

Selected Informal Assessments

This book provides 65 informal assessment instruments that have come to our attention and for which permission to reprint has been granted. The informal assessments included in this book are organized into six sections:

- Self-Advocacy and Self-Determination
- Interpersonal Skills
- Daily Living
- Transportation & Mobility

Table 1   Informal Assessment for Transition Delivery Models

Individual assessment	One on one with individual students • who have special needs • who have unique interests • as a part of counseling and educational planning
Small-group assessment	In group sessions organized • around specific transition needs and interests • to promote in-depth transition planning • for outside of the school day • at community sites
Class assessment	Class assessments • to address basic information that all students need • to integrate the information into the academic content • to assist large groups of students in transition planning in an inclusive setting
Grade-level or school assessment	In advisories or homerooms, conduct informal assessments as a pre- or postactivity for • a school-wide transition fair • course selection for the following school year • selecting community/adult agency speakers • a needs assessment for transition curricula

- Leisure
- Community Participation

These sections represent six areas of assessment that are critical to transition planning, decision making, and instruction. The following paragraphs describe each section in more detail.

Self-Advocacy and Self-Determination

The informal assessments in the "Self-Advocacy and Self-Determination" section focus on measures that describe the individual's self-awareness and self-knowledge of abilities, needs, and rights as well as the individual's ability to plan for short- and long-term goals, to set short-term goals, and to realize his or her goals. Assessments also cover the student's abilities to speak for his or her interests; knowledge of his or her preferences, needs, and satisfaction with life; and ability to act as his or her own advocate. Individual assessments address the various issues of self-esteem, fears, and anger. The assessments may identify personal issues that for some students will require further processing, either in the group or individually. Being aware of the content of each assessment and knowing your students are always helpful in selecting the most appropriate tools. Additional follow-up or services may be needed from support staff at school or in the community.

Interpersonal Skills

The informal assessments in the "Interpersonal Skills and Communication" section provide information to help understand the student's strengths and weaknesses in relating to others in a variety of settings, including home, school, and community. Specific assessments include positive social behaviors such as sharing, cooperation and collaboration, respecting others' privacy and property, knowing socially appropriate and inappropriate behaviors, sensitivity to others' feelings and preferences, sensitivity to multicultural diversity, and environment-specific social behaviors. Some of these assessments will seem more appropriate for individual students rather than group use. Care should be taken to ensure a safe climate for discussion of the important issues tapped by these assessments. A variety of methods for increasing skills in this area should be available through collaboration with school and community support services.

Daily Living

From personal hygiene to basic home maintenance, the "Daily Living Skills" section includes informal assessments to analyze students' functional skills, define attitudes, and establish readiness for independent living. Assessments target such skills as more advanced dressing skills, personal hygiene skills, basic food preparation, and care and maintenance of clothing.

Transportation & Mobility

Accessing public transportation, navigating in the community, and displaying safe driving habits are skills addressed by informal assessments in the "Transportation & Mobility" section.

Leisure

The informal assessments in the "Leisure" section focus on determining preferences for leisure activities and assessing skills in enjoying entertainment and social situations.

Community Participation

The informal assessments in the "Community Participation" section cover topics such as knowing about and being able to access community services, government, and agencies. Further assessment topics in this area include the nature and extent of the student's activities outside the home and school settings.

A Final Note

Transition planning is critical for all students and is a shared responsibility among all educators, students and their families, and their communities. The literature and the legislation have shown that successful transitions are related to a multitude of factors that include independent living and community participation. From early in elementary school through graduation from high school and involvement in postsecondary, career, and community activities, there are many opportunities to favorably influence the successful transition of students. It is our desire that these informal assessments assist you in your efforts.

References

Clark, G. M. (in press). Transition assessment for planning with secondary-level students with learning disabilities. In G. Blalock, J. R. Patton, P. Kohler, & D. Bassett (Eds.), *Transition and students with learning disabilities* (2nd ed.). Austin, TX: PRO-ED.

Clark, G. M. (2007). *Assessment for transitions planning* (2nd ed.). Austin, TX: PRO-ED.

Cronin, M. E., & Patton, J. R. (1993). *Life skills instruction for all students with special needs: A practical guide for integrating real-life content into the curriculum.* Austin, TX: PRO-ED.

Education for All Handicapped Children Act of 1975, 20 U.S.C. §1400 *et seq.* (1975).

Halpern, A. S. (1985). Transition: A look at the foundations. *Exceptional Children, 51,* 479–486.

Individuals with Disabilities Education Improvement Act of 2004, 20 U.S.C. § 1400 *et seq.* (2004) (reauthorization of Individuals with Disabilities Education Act of 1990).

Kokaska, C. J., & Brolin, D. E. (1985). *Career education for handicapped individuals* (2nd ed.). Columbus, OH: Merrill.

Miller, R. J., Lombard, R. C., & Corbey, S. A. (2007). *Transition assessment: Planning transition and IEP development for youth with mild to moderate disabilities.* Boston: Pearson/Allyn & Bacon.

Sitlington, P. L., & Clark, G. M., (2005). *Transition education and services for adolescents with disabilities* (4th ed.). Boston: Allyn & Bacon.

Sitlington, P. L., Neubert, D. A., Begun, W., Lombard, R. C., & Leconte, P. J. (2007). *Assess for success: Handbook on transition assessment* (2nd ed.). Longmont, CO: Sopris West.

Self-Advocacy & Self-Determination
List of Inventories

Name _____ Date _____

Expectations About Events in My Life

☀ **Put a check mark in the column that best matches your feelings about each statement.**

	Strongly Disagree	Disagree	Neutral	Agree	Strongly Agree
1. I find it difficult to talk in front of a group.	☐	☐	☐	☐	☐
2. Whether or not I get into a car accident depends mostly on how good a driver I am.	☐	☐	☐	☐	☐
3. I prefer to be a leader rather than a follower.	☐	☐	☐	☐	☐
4. Other people usually follow my ideas.	☐	☐	☐	☐	☐
5. What happens in my life is mostly determined by powerful people.	☐	☐	☐	☐	☐
6. I try to avoid situations in which someone else tells me what to do.	☐	☐	☐	☐	☐
7. I can usually organize people to get things done.	☐	☐	☐	☐	☐
8. To a great extent, my life is controlled by accidental happenings.	☐	☐	☐	☐	☐
9. I enjoy political participation because I want to have as much say as possible in running government.	☐	☐	☐	☐	☐
10. I am often a leader in groups.	☐	☐	☐	☐	☐
11. When I get what I want, it's usually because I worked hard for it.	☐	☐	☐	☐	☐
12. Whether or not I get to be a leader depends mostly on my ability.	☐	☐	☐	☐	☐
13. I prefer a job in which I have a lot of control over what I do and when I do it.	☐	☐	☐	☐	☐
14. I enjoy being able to influence the actions of others.	☐	☐	☐	☐	☐
15. When I make plans, I am most certain to make them work.	☐	☐	☐	☐	☐
16. I would rather not try something I'm not good at.	☐	☐	☐	☐	☐
17. In order to have my plans work, I make sure that they fit in with the desires of people who have power over me.	☐	☐	☐	☐	☐
18. I am careful to check everything on an automobile before I leave for a long trip.	☐	☐	☐	☐	☐
19. Often, I can't prevent bad things from happening to me.	☐	☐	☐	☐	☐
20. Sometimes politics and government seem so complicated that a person like me can't really understand what's going on.	☐	☐	☐	☐	☐
21. Others usually know what is best for me.	☐	☐	☐	☐	☐
22. When I get what I want, it's usually because I'm lucky.	☐	☐	☐	☐	☐
23. I have a pretty good understanding of the important political issues that confront our society.	☐	☐	☐	☐	☐

Source: "The Desirability of Control," by J. M. Burger and H. M. Cooper, 1979, *Motivation and Emotion, 3/4,* (pp. 381–393). Copyright 1979 by Springer Netherlands, and "Activism and Powerful Others: Distinctions Within the Concept of Internal–External Control," by H. Levenson, 1974, *Journal of Personality Assessment, 38,* pp. 377–383. Copyright 1979 by H. Levenson. Adapted with permission.

	Strongly Disagree	Disagree	Neutral	Agree	Strongly Agree
24. I enjoy making my own decisions.	☐	☐	☐	☐	☐
25. Although I might have good ability, I will not be given leadership without appealing to those in positions of power.	☐	☐	☐	☐	☐
26. People like me are generally well qualified to participate in the political activity and decision making in our country.	☐	☐	☐	☐	☐
27. I enjoy having control over my own destiny.	☐	☐	☐	☐	☐
28. How many friends I have depends on how nice a person I am.	☐	☐	☐	☐	☐
29. It hardly makes any difference who I vote for because whoever gets elected does whatever he/she wants to do anyway.	☐	☐	☐	☐	☐
30. I would rather someone else took over the leadership role when I'm involved in a group project.	☐	☐	☐	☐	☐
31. I have often found that what is going to happen, will happen.	☐	☐	☐	☐	☐
32. There are plenty of ways for people like me to have a say in what our government does.	☐	☐	☐	☐	☐
33. My life is determined by my own actions.	☐	☐	☐	☐	☐
34. I consider myself to be generally more capable of handling situations than others are.	☐	☐	☐	☐	☐
35. My life is chiefly controlled by powerful others.	☐	☐	☐	☐	☐
36. So many other people are active in local issues and organizations that it doesn't matter much to me whether I participate or not.	☐	☐	☐	☐	☐
37. I'd rather run my own business and make my own mistakes than listen to someone else's orders.	☐	☐	☐	☐	☐
38. Whether or not I get into a car accident is mostly a matter of luck.	☐	☐	☐	☐	☐
39. Most public officials wouldn't listen to me, no matter what I did.	☐	☐	☐	☐	☐
40. I like to get a good idea of what a job is all about before I begin.	☐	☐	☐	☐	☐
41. People like me have very little chance of protecting their personal interests when they conflict with those of strong pressure groups.	☐	☐	☐	☐	☐
42. A good many local elections aren't important enough to bother with.	☐	☐	☐	☐	☐
43. It's chiefly a matter of fate whether or not I have few or many friends.	☐	☐	☐	☐	☐
44. When I see a problem, I prefer to do something about it rather than sit by and let it continue.	☐	☐	☐	☐	☐
45. It's not always wise for me to plan too far ahead, because many things turn out to be a matter of good or bad fortune.	☐	☐	☐	☐	☐
46. When it comes to orders, I would rather give them than receive them.	☐	☐	☐	☐	☐
47. Getting what I want requires pleasing those people above me.	☐	☐	☐	☐	☐
48. I wish I could push many of life's daily decisions off on someone else.	☐	☐	☐	☐	☐
49. Whether or not I get to be a leader depends on whether I'm lucky enough to be in the right place at the right time.	☐	☐	☐	☐	☐

Source: "The Desirability of Control," by J. M. Burger and H. M. Cooper, 1979, *Motivation and Emotion, 3/4,* (pp. 381–393). Copyright 1979 by Springer Netherlands, and "Activism and Powerful Others: Distinctions Within the Concept of Internal–External Control," by H. Levenson, 1974, *Journal of Personality Assessment, 38,* pp. 377–383. Copyright 1979 by H. Levenson. Adapted with permission.

	Strongly Disagree	Disagree	Neutral	Agree	Strongly Agree
50. When driving, I try to avoid putting myself in situations where I could be hurt by someone else's mistake.	☐	☐	☐	☐	☐
51. If important people were to decide they didn't like me, I probably wouldn't make any friends.	☐	☐	☐	☐	☐
52. I prefer to avoid situations where someone else has to tell me what I should be doing.	☐	☐	☐	☐	☐
53. I can pretty much determine what will happen in my life.	☐	☐	☐	☐	☐
54. There are many situations in which I would prefer only one choice rather than having to make a decision.	☐	☐	☐	☐	☐
55. I am usually able to protect my personal interests.	☐	☐	☐	☐	☐
56. I like to wait and see if someone else is going to solve a problem so that I don't have to be bothered by it.	☐	☐	☐	☐	☐
57. Whether or not I get into a car accident depends mostly on the other driver.	☐	☐	☐	☐	☐

Source: "The Desirability of Control," by J. M. Burger and H. M. Cooper, 1979, *Motivation and Emotion, 3/4,* (pp. 381–393). Copyright 1979 by Springer Netherlands, and "Activism and Powerful Others: Distinctions Within the Concept of Internal–External Control," by H. Levenson, 1974, *Journal of Personality Assessment, 38,* pp. 377–383. Copyright 1979 by H. Levenson. Adapted with permission.

Name _____   Date _____

Getting To Know Myself

1 How do your peers treat you because of your disability or health problems?

_____

_____

_____

2 How do you feel about the way your peers respond to your disability or health problems?

_____

_____

_____

3 What are your strengths or interests?

_____

_____

_____

4 How can you use your strengths or interests to feel useful or establish new friendships?

_____

_____

_____

5 What kinds of activities would you like to become involved in at school or in the community?

_____

_____

_____

6 What are your hopes and dreams for the future?

_____

_____

_____

Source: Adolescent Psychotherapy Homework Planner (2nd ed., p. 148), by A. E. Jongsma, Jr., L. M. Peterson, and W. P. McInnis, 2006, Hoboken, NJ: John Wiley & Sons. Copyright 2006 by Arthur E. Jongsma, Jr.

Name _____ Date _____

Self-Determination

☼ **Read each statement. If the statement describes you or your beliefs, put a check mark in the column "That's Me." If the statement does not describe you or your beliefs, put a check mark in the column "That's Not Me."**

	That's Me	That's Not Me
1. I am a dreamer.	☐	☐
2. I know what is important to me.	☐	☐
3. I have the right to decide what I want to do.	☐	☐
4. When I do not get something I want, I try a new approach.	☐	☐
5. I forget to take care of my needs when I am with my friends.	☐	☐
6. To help me the next time, I evaluate how things turned out.	☐	☐
7. There are no interesting possibilities in my future.	☐	☐
8. Nothing is important to me.	☐	☐
9. No one has the right to tell me what to do.	☐	☐
10. I can think of only one way to get something I want.	☐	☐
11. I can be successful even though I have weaknesses.	☐	☐
12. I can figure out how to get something if I want it.	☐	☐
13. Sometimes I need to take risks.	☐	☐
14. I do not have any goals for school this year.	☐	☐
15. I would not practice in my mind giving a speech to a class because it would just make me nervous.	☐	☐
16. I do not know my weaknesses.	☐	☐
17. My weaknesses stop me from being successful.	☐	☐
18. I do things without a plan.	☐	☐
19. I know my strengths.	☐	☐
20. I do not know where to find help when I need it.	☐	☐
21. It is a waste of time to reflect on why things turned out the way they did.	☐	☐
22. I dream about what my life will be like after I finish school.	☐	☐
23. I tell others what I want.	☐	☐
24. If I want something, I keep working for it.	☐	☐
25. I think about how I could have done something better.	☐	☐
26. I make decisions without knowing if I have options.	☐	☐
27. I forget to think about what is good for me when I do things.	☐	☐
28. I am frequently surprised by what happens when I do things.	☐	☐ |➜

Source: Self-Determination Student Scale (pp. 1–5), by A. Hoffman, S. L. Field, and S. Sawilowsky, 1995, Austin, TX: PRO-ED. Copyright 1995 by PRO-ED, Inc. Adapted with permission.

29. I am too shy to tell others what I want. .... ☐ ☐

30. I am too scared to take risks. .... ☐ ☐

31. Criticism makes me angry. .... ☐ ☐

32. I am embarrassed when I succeed. .... ☐ ☐

33. I plan to explore many options before choosing a career. .... ☐ ☐

34. I prefer to negotiate rather than to demand or give in. .... ☐ ☐

35. I would rather have the teacher assign me a topic for a project than to create one myself. .... ☐ ☐

36. I am unhappy with who I am. .... ☐ ☐

37. My life has no direction. .... ☐ ☐

38. I imagine myself failing before I do things. .... ☐ ☐

39. I like to know my options before making a decision. .... ☐ ☐

40. I think about what is good for me when I do things. .... ☐ ☐

41. Before I do something, I think about what might happen. .... ☐ ☐

42. My friends are lucky to know me. .... ☐ ☐

43. I know what grades I am working toward in my classes. .... ☐ ☐

44. Doing well in school does not make me feel good. .... ☐ ☐

45. When I want something different from my friend, we find a solution that makes us both happy. .. ☐ ☐

46. It is important for me to know what I do well in being a good friend. .... ☐ ☐

47. In an argument, I am responsible for how I act on my feelings. .... ☐ ☐

48. I wish someone would tell me what to do when I finish school. .... ☐ ☐

49. I like who I am. .... ☐ ☐

50. Goals give my life direction. .... ☐ ☐

51. I imagine myself being successful. .... ☐ ☐

52. Personal hygiene is important to me. .... ☐ ☐

53. My experiences in school will not affect my career choice. .... ☐ ☐

54. When I am with friends, I tell them what I want to do. .... ☐ ☐

55. If I am unable to solve a puzzle quickly, I get frustrated and stop. .... ☐ ☐

56. I make changes to improve my relationship with my family. .... ☐ ☐

57. I do not know if my parents' beliefs are important to me. .... ☐ ☐

58. If I need help with a school project, I can figure out where to get it. .... ☐ ☐

59. I am easily discouraged when I fail. .... ☐ ☐

60. I do things the same way I usually do, even if there might be a better way. ...... ☐ ☐

61. I know what is important when choosing my friends. .... ☐ ☐

62. I could not describe my strengths and weaknesses in school. .... ☐ ☐

63. I like to solve puzzles. .... ☐ ☐ ➲

Source: Self-Determination Student Scale (pp. 1–5), by A. Hoffman, S. L. Field, and S. Sawilowsky, 1995, Austin, TX: PRO-ED. Copyright 1995 by PRO-ED, Inc. Adapted with permission.

64. Nothing good could come from admitting to myself that I am having difficulty in a class. .... ☐ ☐

65. At the end of the marking period, I compare my grades to the grades I expected. .... ☐ ☐

66. It is silly to dream about what I will do when I finish school. .... ☐ ☐

67. I do not participate in school activities because I have nothing to contribute. .... ☐ ☐

68. I accept some criticism and ignore some. .... ☐ ☐

69. I give in when I have differences with others. .... ☐ ☐

70. I do not look back to judge my performance. .... ☐ ☐

71. I tell my friends what I want to do when we go out. .... ☐ ☐

72. I know how to compensate for my weakness in sports. .... ☐ ☐

73. I ask directions or look at a map before going to a new place. .... ☐ ☐

74. I like to be called on in class. .... ☐ ☐

75. When I am angry with my friends, I talk with them about it. .... ☐ ☐

76. I like it when my friends see me do well. .... ☐ ☐

77. When going through the cafeteria line, I pick the first thing. .... ☐ ◇

78. I know how to get help when I need it. .... ☐ ☐

79. I prefer to flip through pages rather than use the index. .... ☐ ☐

80. I think about how well I did something. .... ☐ ☐

81. I do not volunteer in class because I will be embarrassed if I am wrong. .... ☐ ☐

82. I do not know where to get help to decide what I should do after I finish school. .... ☐ ☐

83. If my friends criticize something I am wearing, I would not wear it again. .... ☐ ☐

84. I do not like to review my test results. .... ☐ ☐

85. Before I give a report in class, I go over it in my mind. .... ☐ ☐

86. I talk about people without considering how it might affect them. .... ☐ ☐

87. I feel proud when I succeed. .... ☐ ☐

88. When we are deciding what to do, I just listen to my friends. .... ☐ ☐

89. When deciding what to do with my friend, it is not possible for both of us to be satisfied. .... ☐ ☐

90. When I want good grades, I work until I get them. .... ☐ ☐

91. If my team wins, there is nothing to be gained by reviewing my performance. .... ☐ ☐

92. Before starting a part-time job or extracurricular activity, I think about how it might
affect my school work. .... ☐ ☐

Source: Self-Determination Student Scale (pp. 1–5), by A. Hoffman, S. L. Field, and S. Sawilowsky, 1995, Austin, TX: PRO-ED. Copyright 1995 by PRO-ED, Inc. Adapted with permission.

Name _____   Date _____

Self-Determination Checklist

☀ **Put a check mark in the column that best describes how often you show each skill.**

	Always	Sometimes	Never
1. I recognize and accept my strengths and weaknesses.	❏	❏	❏
2. I can describe my interests.	❏	❏	❏
3. I make most of my decisions.	❏	❏	❏
4. I set my own goals.	❏	❏	❏
5. I work toward my goals.	❏	❏	❏
6. I solve the problems that come up in my life.	❏	❏	❏
7. I take responsibility for what I have done.	❏	❏	❏
8. I speak up when I want to.	❏	❏	❏
9. I say "I'm sorry" when I do something wrong.	❏	❏	❏
10. I say "No" when a request is inappropriate.	❏	❏	❏
11. I manage my time to stay on task until a project is done.	❏	❏	❏
12. I can describe skills for a job.	❏	❏	❏
13. I work independently.	❏	❏	❏
14. I finish my work on time.	❏	❏	❏
15. I am confident in my abilities to communicate with others.	❏	❏	❏
16. I use eye contact while talking.	❏	❏	❏
17. I listen carefully when talking with others.	❏	❏	❏
18. I express myself to others appropriately.	❏	❏	❏
19. I tell others how I feel.	❏	❏	❏
20. I ask others for help.	❏	❏	❏
21. I offer to help others.	❏	❏	❏
22. I share my ideas with others.	❏	❏	❏
23. I can negotiate with others.	❏	❏	❏
24. I accept advice from others.	❏	❏	❏
25. I work well with others.	❏	❏	❏

Source: Adapted and used with permission of Chia-ten Liu and Joung-Min Kim.

Name _____   Date _____

I Am

1. Three words that fit me best are _____, _____, and

   _____.

2. What I like best about me is _____

   _____

3. Some of my favorite things (colors, foods, hobbies, music, books, etc.) are _____

   _____

4. If I were to choose a song that tells how I am feeling right now, it would be _____

   _____

5. The one thing I would like most to change about myself is _____

   _____

6. A couple of ideas I have about how I can start making some changes in my life are _____

   _____

7. The most surprising thing I've found out about myself is _____

   _____

8. How I feel about this surprising discovery is _____

   _____

9. What I fear most is _____

   _____

10. I think the best thing to do about this fear is _____

    _____

Self-Advocacy & Self-Determination ◈

11. Five things I would like most to do or experience in the next month or so are

- ◼ _____
- ◼ _____
- ◼ _____
- ◼ _____
- ◼ _____

12. I don't think I want to _____

_____

13. When I am really down, some people I can count on to understand and listen and even try to help are _____

_____

14. If I had to be anyone else in the world, I would choose to be _____

_____

15. I chose that person because _____

_____

16. Some ideas I have that might help me gain some of the characteristics I admire in another person are _____

_____

17. I know some things about myself, and what I most want to do starting today is _____

_____

Name _____   Date _____

Values That Are Important to Me

☀ **Show how important each value is to you by putting check marks before the value.**

_____ = Not important   __✓__ = Somewhat important   __✓✓__ = Extremely important

_____ **1.** Having a lot of money

_____ **2.** Doing well in school

_____ **3.** Having a lot of friends

_____ **4.** Having one close friend

_____ **5.** Getting along with my parents

_____ **6.** Getting along with my family

_____ **7.** Having time to myself

_____ **8.** Not worrying about having enough to eat

_____ **9.** Getting/having a good job

_____ **10.** Liking my job

_____ **11.** Respecting myself

_____ **12.** Being respected by others

_____ **13.** Having my own space/room

_____ **14.** Being good at something

_____ **15.** Having a clean room

_____ **16.** Breathing clean air

_____ **17.** Recycling

_____ **18.** Having a good education

_____ **19.** Being in good health

_____ **20.** Being handsome/pretty

_____ **21.** Knowing that someone loves me

_____ **22.** Being in love

_____ **23.** Having nice clothes

_____ **24.** Having a lot of possessions

_____ **25.** Being in good physical shape

_____ **26.** Having a boyfriend/girlfriend

_____ **27.** Being good at sports

_____ **28.** Helping others

_____ **29.** Being recognized for helping others

_____ **30.** Believing in God

_____ **31.** Being happy

_____ **32.** Being able to handle responsibility

_____ **33.** Setting goals for myself

_____ **34.** Having control of what happens to me

Source: Life Skills Activities for Secondary Students with Special Needs (p. 373), by D. Mannix, 1995, West Nyack, NY: The Center for Applied Research in Education. Copyright 1995 by The Center for Applied Research in Education. Adapted with permission.

Name _____   Date _____

Yes I Can

☼ **Indicate how much you agree with each statement by putting a check mark in the appropriate column.**

Strongly Disagree	Disagree	Agree	Strongly Agree	
☐	☐	☐	☐	**1.** People with disabilities become upset more easily than people without disabilities.
☐	☐	☐	☐	**2.** People should expect just as much from students with disabilities as from students without disabilities.
☐	☐	☐	☐	**3.** The worst thing that could happen to a person would be for him or her to have a disability.
☐	☐	☐	☐	**4.** People with disabilities can be as successful as people without disabilities.
☐	☐	☐	☐	**5.** People with disabilities resent people who do not have disabilities.
☐	☐	☐	☐	**6.** People with disabilities become discouraged easily.
☐	☐	☐	☐	**7.** People with disabilities should be allowed to participate in programs offered in the community, such as Parks and Recreation programs.
☐	☐	☐	☐	**8.** People with disabilities can take care of themselves.
☐	☐	☐	☐	**9.** People with disabilities can have a normal social life.
☐	☐	☐	☐	**10.** People with disabilities prefer to be with other people with disabilities.
☐	☐	☐	☐	**11.** People with severe disabilities are harder to get along with than people with minor disabilities.
☐	☐	☐	☐	**12.** People with disabilities need more affection and praise than other people do.
☐	☐	☐	☐	**13.** People with disabilities should not expect to lead normal lives.
☐	☐	☐	☐	**14.** People with disabilities should not be fired for reasons having to do with their disabilities.
☐	☐	☐	☐	**15.** People with disabilities should have accommodations available so that they can participate in community activities.

Source: The Yes I Can Social Inclusion Program: Enhancing the Social Inclusion of Young Adults with Developmental Disabilities (p. 67), by B. Abery, 1995, Minneapolis, MN: University of Minnesota, Institute on Community Integration. Copyright 1995 by Brian Abery. Adapted with permission.

Name _____   Date _____

Self-Esteem Profile

☀ **This profile is designed to help you examine six key areas in your life and the experiences in each that account for how you feel about yourself. Read each statement, then circle T for true or F for false to indicate whether it is an accurate or inaccurate description of yourself.**

Physical Safety

T F **1.** I like the neighborhood I live in. I feel safe there.

T F **2.** I like my home and always feel safe there.

T F **3.** I like the school I go to; I always feel safe there.

T F **4.** I'm not afraid of any student at school.

T F **5.** I seldom go to the nurse's office because of a headache or stomachache.

T F **6.** I always make wise choices for the health of my body.

T F **7.** I have a healthy, strong, and fit body.

T F **8.** My parents discipline fairly.

T F **9.** I feel safe when I am at school.

T F **10.** I'm not afraid of anyone in my neighborhood.

Emotional Security

T F **1.** I am a self-confident person.

T F **2.** I am able to laugh at my own mistakes.

T F **3.** It helps to talk about my feelings.

T F **4.** I am my own best friend.

T F **5.** I expect good things to happen to me.

T F **6.** When I mess up, I just try to do it right the next time.

T F **7.** I give myself credit when I do something well.

T F **8.** I do not think it's important to do everything well.

T F **9.** I try never to make fun of others or tease them unfairly.

T F **10.** I know how to manage stress and pressure.

Identity, Self-hood

T F **1.** I am a happy person.

T F **2.** I seldom wish I could be someone else.

T F **3.** I like the way I look.

T F **4.** I like who I am.

T F **5.** I like my body.

T F **6.** I rarely think that if I had more money I would be a lot happier and have more friends.

T F **7.** I can take care of my appearance, trying to look my best every day.

T F **8.** When something good happens to me, I feel I deserve it.

T F **9.** I feel comfortable in most situations, even new ones.

T F **10.** I often compliment others.

Belonging, Affiliation

T F **1.** I have at least two good friends.

T F **2.** Other people are willing to give me help when I need it.

T F **3.** Whenever I say I will do something, people know I can be counted on.

T F **4.** When good things happen to my friends, I'm happy for them.

T F **5.** I like most of the people I know, even if we aren't good friends.

T F **6.** I'm able to hang out with whom I want. I can pick and choose my friends.

T F **7.** Not all my friends are like me.

Source: You & Self-Esteem: The Key to Happiness & Success (pp. 5–7), by B. Youngs, 1992, Austin, TX: PRO-ED. Copyright 1992 by PRO-ED, Inc. Adapted with permission.

T F 8. I'm not intimidated by those who tease me and make fun of me.

T F 9. My friends can count on me for compliments when they have done something well.

T F 10. Others want to include me in what they are doing.

Competence

T F 1. I believe people who set goals get what they want out of life.

T F 2. I know how to set priorities and manage my time.

T F 3. I'm smart enough to do what I want when I put my mind to it.

T F 4. I ask others for help when I need it.

T F 5. I take my problems one step at a time.

T F 6. I can make wise choices and good decisions.

T F 7. I listen to the other person's point of view before I decide what to say.

T F 8. When I have trouble paying attention, I just refocus.

T F 9. I don't feel that I always have to do well in everything; sometimes, giving it my best is enough.

T F 10. I feel capable of coping with life's challenges.

Mission, Purpose

T F 1. I often think about my future and what it will be like.

T F 2. My life has meaning and direction.

T F 3. Whether I succeed or fail is up to me.

T F 4. I know that I'm going to get what I want out of life.

T F 5. I know what I want to do with my life.

T F 6. I have thought about what I want out of life.

T F 7. I am excited about my present life and look forward to my future.

T F 8. I've thought about what kind of a lifestyle I want to live.

T F 9. There are a lot of things I'm interested in.

T F 10. I have goals, and I'm going to achieve them.

Source: You & Self-Esteem: The Key to Happiness & Success (pp. 5–7), by B. Youngs, 1992, Austin, TX: PRO-ED. Copyright 1992 by PRO-ED, Inc. Adapted with permission.

Name _____   Date _____

Me and My Future

☀ **Read each sentence and ask yourself, "Is this how I feel about myself?" Mark the box in the column that matches how much you agree or disagree with each statement.**

	STRONGLY DISAGREE	DISAGREE	AGREE	STRONGLY AGREE
1. I have control over what will happen in my future.	❑	❑	❑	❑
2. It is my parents' job to plan what will happen for me.	❑	❑	❑	❑
3. I can make my life better.	❑	❑	❑	❑
4. I don't think about my future after school because it is far away.	❑	❑	❑	❑
5. With help, I can plan for my future.	❑	❑	❑	❑
6. It is my teachers' job to plan what will happen for me.	❑	❑	❑	❑
7. I have control over what is in my IEP.	❑	❑	❑	❑
8. Luck will play a big part in what my future looks like.	❑	❑	❑	❑
9. If I work hard enough, I can meet my goals.	❑	❑	❑	❑
10. If I have a good future, it will be because of luck.	❑	❑	❑	❑
11. I will be able to handle what happens to me after high school.	❑	❑	❑	❑
12. What happens in my future depends upon what others decide for me (for example, teachers or parents).	❑	❑	❑	❑
13. If I work hard now, I will have a better future.	❑	❑	❑	❑
14. It is my teachers' or parents' fault if things do not work out for me.	❑	❑	❑	❑
15. With planning and hard work, anything is possible.	❑	❑	❑	❑
16. It is my fault if things do not work out for me.	❑	❑	❑	❑
17. If my preferences are not in my IEP, it is because I did not let my parents or teachers know.	❑	❑	❑	❑
18. Planning for my future isn't important.	❑	❑	❑	❑
19. I feel that I can plan for almost anything in my life.	❑	❑	❑	❑
20. My teachers and parents have taught me to be a good planner.	❑	❑	❑	❑

Source: Adapted and used with permission of Jason Rehfeldt.

Name _____   Date _____

Things I Would Like To See in My Transition Plan

☼ **Put a ✓ in the column that shows your preference for areas to be included in your transition plan.**

Recreation		I would like to consider this.	No way!	I need more information.
	Independent sports, activities			
	City/county operated activities			
	Church activities			
	Activities with my friends			
	Activities with my family			

Employment		I would like to consider this.	No way!	I need more information.
	Independent employment			
	Area of interest			
	Job coach			
	Work crew			
	Help finding a job			

Living Arrangements		I would like to consider this.	No way!	I need more information.
	Living on my own			
	Continue living with my parents			
	Group home			
	Supervised apartment			
	Roommate			

	I would like to consider this.	No way!	I need more information.
Community Participation			
Using banks, credit unions			
Using bus system			
Driving			
Buying what I need			
Getting medical attention			

	I would like to consider this.	No way!	I need more information.
Post High School Training			
Technical training			
Community college			
University			
Other training			
Military			

Student _____ Parent/Guardian _____

Conference Leader _____ Date _____

Transition Conference Question Guide

Student Questions

1. What kind of job, career training, or additional education would you like to start after you finish school?

   _____

2. What are your strongest employment or career skills?

   _____

3. What are your strongest independent living skills?

   _____

4. What are your strengths in taking care of your medical, dental, or health needs?

   _____

5. What do you know about locating and using community resources?

   _____

6. What travel or transportation skills do you want to learn or improve?

   _____

7. What do you like to do for leisure and recreation?

   _____

8. What goals do you want to work on to help you get along better with other people?

   _____

9. Knowing how to handle, save, and budget money is very important. What do you consider your strongest financial skills?

   _____

10. Being an adult citizen in our society carries certain legal rights and responsibilities. What knowledge or skills do you have to meet these responsibilities?

    _____

11. What are your strongest communication skills?

    _____

12. Is there anything you'd like to say about your needs, goals, or plans for the future or any other area you're concerned about?

    _____

Source: The Self-Advocacy Strategy: Transition Skills Lists (pp. 202–204), by A. K. Van Reusen, C. S. Bos, J. B. Schumaker, and D. D. Deshler, 1994, Lawrence KS: Edge Enterprises. Copyright 1994 by Van Reusen, Bos, Schumaker, and Deshler. Adapted with permission.

Parent Questions

1. What do you see as your child's strongest transition or adult-life skills?

   _____

2. What skills would you like your child to improve or learn?

   _____

3. What goals would you like your child to pursue?

   _____

4. What services or agencies would you like to know about to prepare your child to move from school to life as an adult?

   _____

5. Is there anything you'd like to say about your child's transition program or any other area you are concerned about?

   _____

Source: The Self-Advocacy Strategy: Transition Skills Lists (pp. 202–204), by A. K. Van Reusen, C. S. Bos, J. B. Schumaker, and D. D. Deshler, 1994, Lawrence KS: Edge Enterprises. Copyright 1994 by Van Reusen, Bos, Schumaker, and Deshler. Adapted with permission.

Name _____   Date _____

The Self-Directed IEP

☀ **Put a ✓ on the line before the steps you plan to address in the meeting.**
After the meeting, go back and mark the column that shows how well you addressed those steps.

		Did Not Do It	So-So	Great!
_____	**1.** Begin the meeting by stating its purpose.	☐	☐	☐
_____	**2.** Introduce everyone I invited.	☐	☐	☐
_____	**3.** Review my past goals and performance.	☐	☐	☐
_____	**4.** Ask for others' feedback.	☐	☐	☐
_____	**5.** State my school and transition goals.	☐	☐	☐
_____	**6.** Ask questions if I did not understand.	☐	☐	☐
_____	**7.** Address differences in opinion.	☐	☐	☐
_____	**8.** State what supports I'll need.	☐	☐	☐
_____	**9.** Summarize my goals.	☐	☐	☐
_____	**10.** Close the meeting by thanking everyone.	☐	☐	☐
_____	**11.** Make a plan to work on my IEP goals all year.	☐	☐	☐

Comments

_____

_____

_____

_____

Source: The Self-Directed IEP, by J. E. Martin, L. H. Marshall, L. L. Maxson, and P. A. Jerman, 1996, Longmont, CO: Sopris West. Copyright 1996 by Sopris West. Adapted with permission.

Name _____   Date _____

Transition Skills Assessment

☼ Answer each question by circling Y for Yes or N for No in the column that matches your role.

Student	Parent	Teacher	
			## Self-Awareness
Y N	Y N	Y N	Do you participate in your IEP/transition planning?
Y N	Y N	Y N	Do you understand and effectively talk about your limitations/needs as well as strengths?
Y N	Y N	Y N	Do you need ongoing guardian support?
			## Responsibility
Y N	Y N	Y N	Do you complete your school assignments on time?
Y N	Y N	Y N	Do you come to classes regularly and on time?
Y N	Y N	Y N	Do you follow through on things that you tell people you will do?
			## Solving Problems
Y N	Y N	Y N	When you have a problem, do you think of several ways of solving it?
Y N	Y N	Y N	When you can't think of a good way of solving a problem, do you ask other people to help?
Y N	Y N	Y N	After you make a decision, do you follow through on doing what you have decided?
Y N	Y N	Y N	When you get mad at someone, do you solve the problem without yelling or hurting that person?
Y N	Y N	Y N	When you get mad and can't figure out what to do, do you ask for help?

Source: Transition Skills Assessment (pp. 1–7), by Minnesota Interagency Office on Transition Services, 1996, St. Paul, MN: Author. Copyright 1996 by Minnesota Interagency Office on Transition Services. Adapted with permission.

Name _____   Date _____

My IEP; How Did It Go?

☀ **Now that my IEP meeting is over . . .**

1. Overall, I would describe the experience as _____

_____

2. I felt prepared for the meeting.   ___ Yes   ___ No

3. I remembered to take my notes.   ___ Yes   ___ No

4. I had identified my goals for next year.   ___ Yes   ___ No

5. I understood my role as a participant in this meeting.   ___ Yes   ___ No

6. I understood my role as a self-advocate in this meeting. ___ Yes   ___ No

7. I expressed my goals and needs clearly.   ___ Yes   ___ No

   Example _____

8. I negotiated with others well.   ___ Yes   ___ No

   Example _____

9. I resolved problems well.   ___ Yes   ___ No

   Example _____

10. Three things I liked about my participation in this meeting

   ★ _____

   ★ _____

   ★ _____

11. Three things I would do differently next time

   ★ _____

   ★ _____

   ★ _____

Source: Self-Advocacy for Students Who Are Deaf or Hard of Hearing (p. 108), by K. English, 1997, Austin, TX: PRO-ED. Copyright 1997 by PRO-ED, Inc. Adapted with permission.

Name _____   Date _____

Legal Rights Self-Check

☼ **As an adult you are entitled to certain rights. Circle Yes or No to indicate your knowledge of the following rights. Then put a ✓ in the box next to the items you want to learn more about.**

Individual

❑	**1.**	Vote	**Yes No**
❑	**2.**	Marry	**Yes No**
❑	**3.**	Education	**Yes No**
❑	**4.**	Freedom of speech and religion	**Yes No**
❑	**5.**	Free from discrimination due to my disability	**Yes No**
❑	**6.**	Equal opportunities in employment	**Yes No**
❑	**7.**	Considered for employment based upon actual job-related abilities	**Yes No**
❑	**8.**	Accommodations in the workplace, if I qualify as having a significant limitation in a major life function	**Yes No**
❑	**9.**	Equal housing opportunities	**Yes No**
❑	**10.**	Protection from exploitation and abuse	**Yes No**
❑	**11.**	Confidentiality in personal matters	**Yes No**
❑	**12.**	Accommodations in postsecondary education, if I qualify for such services	**Yes No**
❑	**13.**	Americans with Disabilities Act is and what rights I have under it	**Yes No**

Legal *(If suspected or accused of committing a crime)*

❑	**14.**	Remain silent and that anything I say may be used against me in court (This means that I can remain completely silent or answer some questions.)	**Yes No**
❑	**15.**	Telephone a lawyer or family/friends to notify them of your arrest	**Yes No**
❑	**16.**	Consult with an attorney and have that attorney present during questioning (If I cannot afford an attorney, one will be provided at no cost.)	**Yes No**
❑	**17.**	Confront and question anyone who has accused me of a crime	**Yes No**
❑	**18.**	Appeal a legal decision that rules against me	**Yes No**
❑	**19.**	Challenge being held in jail without just cause	**Yes No**
❑	**20.**	Be presumed competent until declared incompetent by a court of law	**Yes No**

☼ **Put a ✓ in the box next to words that you know.**

Words that are used with finding and keeping a job

❑ benefits   ❑ deduction   ❑ harassment

❑ interview   ❑ job description   ❑ policy

❑ promotion   ❑ qualification   ❑ shift

❑ supervisor   ❑ wages

Words that are used if I am considered a suspect for a crime

❑ Miranda warning   ❑ arrest   ❑ detention   ❑ bail

❑ case   ❑ interrogation   ❑ confession   ❑ disposition

❑ proceedings   ❑ testify   ❑ prosecutor   ❑ sentencing

❑ incarceration   ❑ jail   ❑ prison   ❑ probation

Name _____   Date _____

Explaining My Difficulties

☀ **Place a check mark in the column that matches your opinion.**

	Easy for Me	Hard for Me
1. I can explain my difficulties to my teachers.	☐	☐
2. I can explain my difficulties to my employer.	☐	☐
3. I can explain to an employer why I would need a reasonable accommodation for my job.	☐	☐
4. I am comfortable asking an employer to make a reasonable accommodation for my job.	☐	☐
5. I can explain my legal rights that help me in high school.	☐	☐
6. I can explain the laws that will protect my rights when I go to college.	☐	☐
7. I can explain the laws that will protect my rights when I get a job.	☐	☐

Summary

❶ Learning to be a self-advocate takes time and practice.

❶ Practicing personal and interpersonal skills with a strong knowledge base will help in developing confidence and in achieving goals.

Homework

Create a Self-Advocacy File with the following items:

❶ High school transcripts (or a school address to request copies after graduation)

❷ Copies of standardized tests (SATs, etc.)

❸ Résumé

❹ Copies of medical records and phone numbers/addresses of physicians, audiologists, and others

❺ Samples of academic work (essays, art, science projects)

Ask a parent for other ideas on important papers and records to include.

Source: Self-Advocacy for Students Who Are Deaf or Hard of Hearing (p. 18), by K. English, 1997, Austin, TX: PRO-ED. Copyright 1997 by PRO-ED, Inc. Adapted with permission.

Interpersonal Skills

List of Inventories

Name _____ Date _____

Social Skills

Completed by _____

☀ **Put a check mark in the column that indicates how often the student demonstrates the following skills.**

	Never	Sometimes	Always
1. Display behavior that is age appropriate	____	____	____
2. Work effectively under different styles of supervision	____	____	____
3. Work cooperatively as a member of a team	____	____	____
4. Get along and work effectively with people with different personalities	____	____	____
5. Show up regularly and on time for activities and appointments	____	____	____
6. See things from another's point of view	____	____	____
7. Engage appropriately in social interaction and situations	____	____	____
8. Speak with others in a relaxed and self-confident manner	____	____	____
9. Compliment and provide constructive feedback to others at appropriate times	____	____	____
10. Initiate and maintain friendly conversations with another individual	____	____	____
11. Initiate, maintain, and draw others into friendly group conversations	____	____	____
12. Join in friendly group conversations	____	____	____
13. Express complaints appropriately	____	____	____
14. Avoid arguments	____	____	____
15. Help others without being asked	____	____	____
16. Help others when asked	____	____	____
17. Show control of emotions and behaviors	____	____	____
18. Demonstrate appropriate manners in a social setting	____	____	____

Source: "Transition Planning: Developing a Career Portfolio for Students with Disabilities," by M. Sarkees-Wircenski and J. L. Wircenski, 1994, *Career Development for Exceptional Individuals, 17* (2), p. 210. Copyright 1994 by Division on Career Development and Transition of the Council for Exceptional Children. Adapted with permission.

Name _____ Date _____

Personal Life

Answer each question by putting a ✓ in the appropriate column.

	Yes	Sometimes	No

Communicating With Other People

1. Do you look people in the eye when you talk to them or when they talk to you? ❏ ❏ ❏

2. Do you listen carefully to other people when they talk to you, and do you try to understand what they are saying?... ❏ ❏ ❏

3. When you are talking to other people, do you treat them with respect? .... ❏ ❏ ❏

Relating to Authorities

4. If you don't understand what a teacher or employer wants you to do, do you ask questions?.. ❏ ❏ ❏

5. If teachers or employers try to correct something you are doing, do you accept their help?.. ❏ ❏ ❏

6. If you think that a teacher or employer isn't treating you fairly, do you stand up for your rights? .... ❏ ❏ ❏

Relating to Peers

7. Do you get along well with people your own age?........................... ❏ ❏ ❏

8. If something isn't going well with your friends, do you work it out? .... ❏ ❏ ❏

9. If you need something from a friend, do you ask for help?..................... ❏ ❏ ❏

10. If somebody tries to take advantage of you, do you stand up for yourself and stop this from happening? .... ❏ ❏ ❏

Source: Transition Skills Assessment (pp. 1–7), by Minnesota Interagency Office on Transition Services, 1996, St. Paul, MN: Author. Copyright 1996 by Minnesota Interagency Office on Transition Services. Adapted with permission.

Name _____   Date _____

Friends and Relationships

☀ **Put a check mark in the box next to any question that you want to learn more about. Circle Yes or No to answer to each question.**

☐   **1.** Am I happy with the friends I have in my life right now? . . . .   **Yes**   **No**

☐   **2.** Do I know how to make friends that will help me keep my life on track? . . . .   **Yes**   **No**

☐   **3.** Do I know how to talk with people about stuff that is on my mind? . . . .   **Yes**   **No**

☐   **4.** Do I know people who will help me out when I need a hand? . . . .   **Yes**   **No**

☐   **5.** Do I know how to meet new people? . . . .   **Yes**   **No**

☐   **6.** Do I know what I am looking for in a friend? . . . .   **Yes**   **No**

☐   **7.** Do I know how to be a good friend? . . . .   **Yes**   **No**

☐   **8.** Do I know where to find help if someone I know has a problem with anger? . . . .   **Yes**   **No**

☐   **9.** Do I know what I need to know about dating? . . . .   **Yes**   **No**

☐   **10.** Do I know what I need to know about marriage? . . . .   **Yes**   **No**

☐   **11.** Do I know what I need to know about having my own family? . . . .   **Yes**   **No**

Source: Adapted and used with permission of Julie Haffner.

Name _____   Date _____

Peer Interaction Skills

Person completing the form: ❑ Student   ❑ Parent   ❑ Teacher

3 = **Successful**   2 = **Somewhat successful**   1 = **Not successful**

❶ **Does the student have satisfactory peer conversation skills?**

_____ The student faces others and uses appropriate stance and distance.

_____ The student can initiate peer conversations appropriately.

_____ The student can maintain peer conversations and appropriately identify and manage the problems that occur.

_____ The student can terminate peer conversations appropriately and arrange for future contact.

_____ The student can maintain peer conversations without excessive horseplay or silliness.

_____ The student can maintain serious peer conversations when others are acting silly.

_____ The student can conduct peer conversations without using aggressive words or actions.

_____ The student can converse with peers without problematic interruptions, using inappropriate subject matter, or too frequently changing topics.

_____ The student can identify and avoid impediments to conversation.

_____ **Total**

❷ **Can the student participate successfully in peer activities?**

_____ The student participates in peer activities without excessive concern over winning and losing.

_____ The student recognizes that successful participation in activities is necessary to adult living.

_____ The student can initiate peer involvement in activities successfully.

_____ The student can follow the rules without cheating.

_____ The student can cope appropriately with peers who improperly participate in activities.

_____ The student is alert for his or her potential behavior problems during peer activities and knows how to manage the problems that do occur.

_____ The student responds appropriately when he or she believes incorrect decisions are made by the activity authority.

_____ The student is a good winner and loser and is able to compromise.

_____ The student can exit peer activities properly.

_____ **Total**

➡

Source: Peer Interaction Skills, Personal Power: Succeeding with Others (pp. 183–186), by R. H. Wells, 1990, Austin, TX: PRO-ED. Copyright 1990 by PRO-ED, Inc. Adapted with permission.

❸ **Does the student require help making and keeping friends?**

_____ The student uses the behaviors appropriate to being a friend.

_____ The student recognizes that he or she has the potential to be friends to others.

_____ The student recognizes his or her weaknesses as a friend.

_____ The student frequents places where he or she is likely to meet potential friends and can initiate conversations with potential friends.

_____ The student can maintain conversations appropriately with potential friends.

_____ The student can issue invitations to potential friends.

_____ The student performs the responsibilities of a friend.

_____ The student is positive, interesting, and pleasant with friends.

_____ The student avoids quarrels with friends and appropriately ends the quarrels that do occur.

_____ **Total**

❹ **Does the student know how to interact with opposite-sex peers?**

_____ The student is skilled and knowledgeable managing opposite-sex peer interactions.

_____ The student has an appearance appropriate to successful opposite-sex peer interactions.

_____ The student can appropriately initiate and maintain conversations with opposite-sex peers.

_____ The student can exit conversations with opposite-sex peers appropriately.

_____ The student can initiate and implement appropriate activities with opposite-sex peers.

_____ The student is aware of his or her difficulties conversing with opposite-sex peers.

_____ The student limits opposite-sex interactions to appropriate times and places so he or she is not distracted.

_____ The student limits opposite-sex relationship problems to appropriate times and places.

_____ The student recognizes that properly conducted opposite-sex interactions are essential to adult living.

_____ **Total**

❺ **Does the student require help learning to interact nonaggressively?**

_____ The student can distinguish aggressive and nonaggressive behavior and recognize the problems of aggression.

_____ The student recognizes that nonaggressive conduct is necessary to successful daily living.

_____ The student anticipates and avoids using aggressive behaviors.

_____ The student can identify and use many alternatives to aggressive behavior.

_____ The student controls his or her aggressive thoughts when faced with conflict.

_____ The student avoids the use of aggressive language.

_____ The student can refrain from aggressive behavior, even when provoked.

_____ The student can refrain from aggressive behavior, even in difficult situations.

_____ The student recognizes that successful adults must use nonaggressive conduct.

_____ **Total**

Source: Peer Interaction Skills, Personal Power: Succeeding with Others (pp. 183–186), by R. H. Wells, 1990, Austin, TX: PRO-ED. Copyright 1990 by PRO-ED, Inc. Adapted with permission.

3 = Successful   2 = Somewhat successful   1 = Not successful

❻ Does the student require help learning to avoid peer setups?

_____ The student identifies being set up by peers.

_____ The student avoids giving up self-control when a peer attempts to set him or her up.

_____ The student understands that showing a strong response to peer setups encourages additional setups.

_____ The student can identify and use many ways to avoid peer setups.

_____ The student can identify the reasons that peers start setups.

_____ The student is not a regular target of peer setups.

_____ The student can identify and avoid self-setups.

_____ The student can identify and avoid setting up peers.

_____ The student can refrain from involvement in setups, even though peers may sabotage this effort.

_____ **Total**

❼ Does the student require help learning about negative leaders?

_____ The student can identify and avoid negative peer leaders.

_____ The student can identify the consequences of following negative leaders.

_____ The student understands that negative leaders are not really friends.

_____ The student understands that following negative leaders creates but doesn't solve problems.

_____ The student understands that resisting negative leaders is essential to successful adult living.

_____ The student can identify and use alternatives to following negative leaders.

_____ The student does not lead peers negatively.

_____ The student can identify and avoid times and places when he or she is likely to encounter negative leaders.

_____ The student can identify and use alternatives to being a negative leader or follower.

_____ **Total**

❽ Does the student require help avoiding drugs?

_____ The student successfully avoids illegal drug use.

_____ The student is responsive to the drug education offered him or her and recognizes its importance.

_____ The student understands that drugs are problem makers, not problem solvers.

_____ The student recognizes that peer pressure is required only to obtain participation in negative activities, not positive ones.

_____ The student identifies and uses effective responses to peer pressure to use drugs.

_____ The student says no and leaves the area when offered drugs.

_____ The student recognizes the potentially enormous consequences of drug abuse.

_____ The student avoids places where he or she is likely to be offered drugs.

_____ The student can avoid drug abuse, even in difficult situations.

_____ **Total**

Source: Peer Interaction Skills, Personal Power: Succeeding with Others (pp. 183–186), by R. H. Wells, 1990, Austin, TX: PRO-ED. Copyright 1990 by PRO-ED, Inc. Adapted with permission.

3 = Successful   2 = Somewhat successful   1 = Not successful

❾ Does the student require help learning to interact successfully with all peers?

_____   The student can identify and avoid the problems that younger peers sometimes have with older peers.

_____   The student can identify and avoid the problems that older peers sometimes have with younger peers.

_____   The student can identify and use appropriate ways to interact with peers they dislike.

_____   The student recognizes that adults must be able to interact successfully with all peers.

_____   The student interacts appropriately with peers who aren't in their group or clique.

_____   The student understands the role of cliques and can function successfully with or without clique membership.

_____   The student interacts appropriately with peers of different cultural backgrounds.

_____   The student interacts appropriately with special education students.

_____   The student interacts appropriately with peers who are new to their class or community.

_____   **Total**

Peer Interaction Profile

Plot the total score for each sequence on the graph. Up to 27 points can be assigned to a sequence-skill area. Higher scores indicate successful areas, while lower scores represent skill areas in need of intervention.

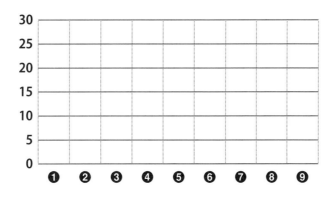

❶ = Peer conversation skills
❷ = Participate peer activities
❸ = Making and keeping friends
❹ = Interact with opposite-sex peers
❺ = Interact nonaggressively
❻ = Avoid peer setups
❼ = Avoid negative leadership
❽ = Avoid drugs
❾ = Interact with all peers

Source: Peer Interaction Skills, Personal Power: Succeeding with Others (pp. 183–186), by R. H. Wells, 1990, Austin, TX: PRO-ED. Copyright 1990 by PRO-ED, Inc. Adapted with permission.

Name _____ Date _____

Social Skills Survey

Person completing the form: ❏ Student ❏ Parent ❏ Teacher

☼ **Answer each question by putting a check mark under the correct heading.**

	1 Never	2 Seldom	3 Sometimes	4 Often	5 Always
1. Can you get other people to see your side of a discussion?	❏	❏	❏	❏	❏
2. Do you ask permission when it's needed?	❏	❏	❏	❏	❏
3. When you apologize, do you give the reason for the apology?	❏	❏	❏	❏	❏
4. Do people understand your directions?	❏	❏	❏	❏	❏
5. Do you apologize when you're at fault?	❏	❏	❏	❏	❏
6. Do you meet your responsibilities?	❏	❏	❏	❏	❏
7. When you take messages, do you include what you were told?	❏	❏	❏	❏	❏
8. Do you engage in conversation easily?	❏	❏	❏	❏	❏
9. Do you accept help when it is offered?	❏	❏	❏	❏	❏
10. Do you think about a question carefully before asking it?	❏	❏	❏	❏	❏
11. Do you feel comfortable asking for information?	❏	❏	❏	❏	❏
12. When someone criticizes you, can you handle the situation without getting upset?	❏	❏	❏	❏	❏
13. Do you give good directions?	❏	❏	❏	❏	❏
14. Can you introduce yourself to people you would like to know?	❏	❏	❏	❏	❏
15. Are you confident knowing where to get information?	❏	❏	❏	❏	❏
16. When people criticize you and you do not understand, do you ask for an explanation?	❏	❏	❏	❏	❏
17. Do you offer to help people when they need it?	❏	❏	❏	❏	❏
18. Do you ask for help to solve problems?	❏	❏	❏	❏	❏
19. Can you tell someone that they did a good job?	❏	❏	❏	❏	❏

➡

Source: Job Related Social Skills: A Curriculum for Adolescents with Special Needs (pp. 31–41), by M. Montague and K. Lund, 1991, Ann Arbor, MI: Exceptional Innovations. Copyright 1991 by Exceptional Innovations. Adapted with permission.

		1 Never	2 Seldom	3 Sometimes	4 Often	5 Always
20.	When you ask for a favor, do you know what to say?	☐	☐	☐	☐	☐
21.	Do you remember to give messages to people?	☐	☐	☐	☐	☐
22.	Do you like it when someone gives you a compliment?	☐	☐	☐	☐	☐
23.	Can you handle other people's complaints graciously?	☐	☐	☐	☐	☐
24.	When you are with friends and meet someone they do not know, do you introduce them?	☐	☐	☐	☐	☐
25.	Is it easy for you to compliment others?	☐	☐	☐	☐	☐
26.	Do you know what to say when someone gives you a compliment?	☐	☐	☐	☐	☐
27.	Do you ask questions when you do not understand something?	☐	☐	☐	☐	☐
28.	Do you help others?	☐	☐	☐	☐	☐
29.	When you feel that you need help, do you ask for it?	☐	☐	☐	☐	☐
30.	Can you convince others of your opinion?	☐	☐	☐	☐	☐
31.	Do you listen carefully to instructions?	☐	☐	☐	☐	☐
32.	Can you start a conversation?	☐	☐	☐	☐	☐
33.	Can people clearly follow your directions?	☐	☐	☐	☐	☐
34.	When someone helps you, do you thank that person?	☐	☐	☐	☐	☐
35.	Do you understand when someone has a complaint?	☐	☐	☐	☐	☐
36.	Do you get to places on time?	☐	☐	☐	☐	☐

Source: Job Related Social Skills: A Curriculum for Adolescents with Special Needs (pp. 31–41), by M. Montague and K. Lund, 1991, Ann Arbor, MI: Exceptional Innovations. Copyright 1991 by Exceptional Innovations. Adapted with permission.

Name _____   Date _____

Social Skills Survey Tally

Skill 1: Ordering Job Responsibilities

	Question 6	Question 36	Total Skill Score
Student	1 2 3 4 5	1 2 3 4 5	
Teacher	1 2 3 4 5	1 2 3 4 5	
Parent	1 2 3 4 5	1 2 3 4 5	

Skill 2: Understanding Instructions

	Question 4	Question 31	Total Skill Score
Student	1 2 3 4 5	1 2 3 4 5	
Teacher	1 2 3 4 5	1 2 3 4 5	
Parent	1 2 3 4 5	1 2 3 4 5	

Skill 3: Making Introductions

	Question 14	Question 24	Total Skill Score
Student	1 2 3 4 5	1 2 3 4 5	
Teacher	1 2 3 4 5	1 2 3 4 5	
Parent	1 2 3 4 5	1 2 3 4 5	

Skill 4: Asking Questions

	Question 10	Question 27	Total Skill Score
Student	1 2 3 4 5	1 2 3 4 5	
Teacher	1 2 3 4 5	1 2 3 4 5	
Parent	1 2 3 4 5	1 2 3 4 5	

Source: Job Related Social Skills: A Curriculum for Adolescents with Special Needs (pp. 31–41), by M. Montague and K. Lund, 1991, Ann Arbor, MI: Exceptional Innovations. Copyright 1991 by Exceptional Innovations. Adapted with permission.

Skill 5: Asking Permission

	Question 2	Question 20	Total Skill Score
Student	1 2 3 4 5	1 2 3 4 5	
Teacher	1 2 3 4 5	1 2 3 4 5	
Parent	1 2 3 4 5	1 2 3 4 5	

Skill 6: Asking for Help

	Question 18	Question 29	Total Skill Score
Student	1 2 3 4 5	1 2 3 4 5	
Teacher	1 2 3 4 5	1 2 3 4 5	
Parent	1 2 3 4 5	1 2 3 4 5	

Skill 7: Accepting Help

	Question 9	Question 34	Total Skill Score
Student	1 2 3 4 5	1 2 3 4 5	
Teacher	1 2 3 4 5	1 2 3 4 5	
Parent	1 2 3 4 5	1 2 3 4 5	

Skill 8: Offering Help

	Question 17	Question 28	Total Skill Score
Student	1 2 3 4 5	1 2 3 4 5	
Teacher	1 2 3 4 5	1 2 3 4 5	
Parent	1 2 3 4 5	1 2 3 4 5	

Skill 9: Requesting Information

	Question 11	Question 15	Total Skill Score
Student	1 2 3 4 5	1 2 3 4 5	
Teacher	1 2 3 4 5	1 2 3 4 5	
Parent	1 2 3 4 5	1 2 3 4 5	

Source: Job Related Social Skills: A Curriculum for Adolescents with Special Needs (pp. 31–41), by M. Montague and K. Lund, 1991, Ann Arbor, MI: Exceptional Innovations. Copyright 1991 by Exceptional Innovations. Adapted with permission.

Skill 10: Taking Messages

	Question 7	Question 21	Total Skill Score
Student	1 2 3 4 5	1 2 3 4 5	
Teacher	1 2 3 4 5	1 2 3 4 5	
Parent	1 2 3 4 5	1 2 3 4 5	

Skill 11: Engaging in a Conversation

	Question 8	Question 32	Total Skill Score
Student	1 2 3 4 5	1 2 3 4 5	
Teacher	1 2 3 4 5	1 2 3 4 5	
Parent	1 2 3 4 5	1 2 3 4 5	

Skill 12: Giving Directions

	Question 13	Question 33	Total Skill Score
Student	1 2 3 4 5	1 2 3 4 5	
Teacher	1 2 3 4 5	1 2 3 4 5	
Parent	1 2 3 4 5	1 2 3 4 5	

Skill 13: Responding to Compliments

	Question 22	Question 26	Total Skill Score
Student	1 2 3 4 5	1 2 3 4 5	
Teacher	1 2 3 4 5	1 2 3 4 5	
Parent	1 2 3 4 5	1 2 3 4 5	

Skill 14: Giving Compliments

	Question 19	Question 25	Total Skill Score
Student	1 2 3 4 5	1 2 3 4 5	
Teacher	1 2 3 4 5	1 2 3 4 5	
Parent	1 2 3 4 5	1 2 3 4 5	

Source: Job Related Social Skills. A Curriculum for Adolescents with Special Needs (pp. 31–41), by M. Montague and K. Lund, 1991, Ann Arbor, MI: Exceptional Innovations. Copyright 1991 by Exceptional Innovations. Adapted with permission.

Skill 15: Convincing Others

	Question 1	Question 30	Total Skill Score
Student	1 2 3 4 5	1 2 3 4 5	
Teacher	1 2 3 4 5	1 2 3 4 5	
Parent	1 2 3 4 5	1 2 3 4 5	

Skill 16: Apologizing

	Question 3	Question 5	Total Skill Score
Student	1 2 3 4 5	1 2 3 4 5	
Teacher	1 2 3 4 5	1 2 3 4 5	
Parent	1 2 3 4 5	1 2 3 4 5	

Skill 17: Accepting Criticism

	Question 12	Question 16	Total Skill Score
Student	1 2 3 4 5	1 2 3 4 5	
Teacher	1 2 3 4 5	1 2 3 4 5	
Parent	1 2 3 4 5	1 2 3 4 5	

Skill 18: Responding to a Complaint

	Question 23	Question 35	Total Skill Score
Student	1 2 3 4 5	1 2 3 4 5	
Teacher	1 2 3 4 5	1 2 3 4 5	
Parent	1 2 3 4 5	1 2 3 4 5	

Source: Job Related Social Skills: A Curriculum for Adolescents with Special Needs (pp. 31–41), by M. Montague and K. Lund, 1991, Ann Arbor, MI: Exceptional Innovations. Copyright 1991 by Exceptional Innovations. Adapted with permission.

Name _____   Date _____

Anger Questionnaire

☀ **Put a check mark in the box next to the statements that are TRUE for you. Then go through the list again and write the letter "P" next to the three statements that reflect your biggest problems.**

☐ I get really angry when people disagree with me.

☐ I do not like to get angry.

☐ I would rather pretend to agree than get into an argument.

☐ I am usually the one to give in during an argument.

☐ I have been known to threaten people.

☐ If I get angry, I feel guilty later.

☐ I would rather keep my anger inside and avoid any trouble.

☐ I always think of better things to say after an argument.

☐ Things seem to make me angry very quickly.

☐ I get nervous when other people are angry.

☐ I just seem to go blank when I am angry, and I can't think clearly.

☐ I just get so angry that I have to hit something.

☐ I hold grudges against people who make me mad.

☐ I ignore people who I am angry with.

☐ If someone is rude to me, I seek revenge later.

☐ I stay angry for a long time.

☐ I can go from being totally calm to completely enraged in minutes.

☐ I usually feel bad after I get angry.

☐ I usually regret my actions when I am angry.

☐ I throw things when I am really angry.

☐ Being angry is not good.

☐ Nice people don't get angry.

☐ I have a hard time forgiving people.

☐ I get so mad that sometimes I don't know what I am doing.

☐ I seem to get angry at even the smallest thing.

☐ After I explode, I feel a lot better.

☐ I tend to lose control when I am angry.

☐ I do not like to admit that I am wrong.

☐ I usually avoid people I am angry with.

☐ I enjoy getting angry.

Source: The Anger Workout Book for Teens (p. 20), by J. Stewart, 2002, Austin, TX: PRO-ED. Copyright 2002 by PRO-ED, Inc. Adapted with permission.

Name _____   Date _____

Taking Inventory of Anger

❶ Describe the most recent incident when you got angry and aggressive.

- When?   Date _____   Time _____

- Where were you? _____

- What happened? _____

- List your thoughts. _____

- Describe your feelings. _____

- Explain what you did. _____

- What was the outcome? _____

- How common is this type of incident for you? ❑ Happens often ❑ Hardly ever happens ❑ Never happened before

❷ How frequently do you get seriously angry and aggressive?

Number of times per day _____   Number of times per week _____   Number of times per month _____

❸ What do you often get angry about? _____

❹ Has your anger ever gotten you in trouble?

- Have you ever been suspended from school because of your anger?   ❑ Yes   ❑ No

- Have you ever been in trouble with the law because of your anger?   ❑ Yes   ❑ No

- Have you ever been banned from a club, sport, or public place because of your anger?   ❑ Yes   ❑ No

❺ What techniques have you tried to help yourself deal effectively with anger? _____

_____

Did they work? Please explain. _____

❻ How often do the following behaviors occur?

	Never	Occasionally	Frequently	Continually
• Swearing at people	❑	❑	❑	❑
• Putting people down	❑	❑	❑	❑
• Breaking things on purpose	❑	❑	❑	❑
• Deliberately hurting people	❑	❑	❑	❑
• Throwing things	❑	❑	❑	❑
• Yelling at people	❑	❑	❑	❑
• Losing control	❑	❑	❑	❑
• Getting revenge	❑	❑	❑	❑
• Feeling like beating people up	❑	❑	❑	❑
• Shoving, hitting, or pushing others	❑	❑	❑	❑

Source: The Anger Workout Book for Teens (pp. 32–33), by J. Stewart, 2002, Austin, TX: PRO-ED. Copyright 2002 by PRO-ED, Inc. Adapted with permission.

Name _____   Date _____

Assertive People

☀ **Circle Yes or No for each statement that shows assertive behavior.**

Yes   No   **1.** Make eye contact with the person who is speaking

Yes   No   **2.** Talk with a firm, clear, friendly, direct voice

Yes   No   **3.** Hide your face so you won't be embarrassed

Yes   No   **4.** Stand or sit up straight

Yes   No   **5.** Yell or scream so you get everybody's attention

Yes   No   **6.** Be prepared to talk about what you need

Yes   No   **7.** Start crying if you don't get your way

Yes   No   **8.** Find out who you need to talk to about your problem

Yes   No   **9.** Take a friend with you if you feel afraid or nervous

Yes   No   **10.** Do not worry about what the laws say, because they are too confusing

Yes   No   **11.** Ask if there is an appeal process

Yes   No   **12.** Do not take no for an answer

Yes   No   **13.** Ask for help if you can't solve the problem yourself

Yes   No   **14.** Give up and go home

Source: Whose Future Is It Anyway?, by M. Wehmeyer and K. Kelchner, 1995, Arlington, TX: The Arc. Copyright 1995 by The Arc. Adapted with permission.

Name _____ Date _____

Assertiveness Can Be Difficult

☼ **Use this scale to answer each question.**

3 = I have no problem asserting myself.
2 = I am able to assert myself most of the time.
1 = I have extreme difficulty asserting myself.

	3	2	1
1. Asking your teacher or supervisor a question	3	2	1
2. Asking a friend not to smoke around you	3	2	1
3. Disciplining a child you are babysitting	3	2	1
4. Asking your supervisor for a raise	3	2	1
5. Starting a conversation with a stranger	3	2	1
6. Resisting pressure to have sex	3	2	1
7. Asking your friend to return something he or she borrowed	3	2	1
8. Returning an item to a store	3	2	1
9. Giving a compliment	3	2	1
10. Asking a teacher for clarification on an assignment	3	2	1
11. Resisting sales pressure	3	2	1
12. Asking a friend to return borrowed money	3	2	1
13. Starting a conversation at a party	3	2	1
14. Asking your doctor or dentist questions	3	2	1
15. Refusing a request made by a relative	3	2	1
16. Asking a fellow student the purpose of a request	3	2	1
17. Resisting pressure to drink or use drugs	3	2	1
18. Refusing a request from an organization of which you are a member	3	2	1
19. Giving a friend a compliment	3	2	1
20. Taking a stand on a controversial issue at home, school, or work	3	2	1
21. Asking a friend for a favor	3	2	1
22. Obtaining sales help in a busy store	3	2	1
23. Saying no to someone who asks you out on a date	3	2	1
24. Choosing a movie for a group of friends to see	3	2	1

Source: Community Living Skill Workbook for the Head Injured Adult, by D. K. Angle and J. M. Buxton, 1991, Austin, TX: PRO-ED. Copyright 1991 by PRO-ED, Inc. Adapted with permission.

Name _____   Date _____

Empathy Quotient

	Strongly Agree	Slightly Agree	Slightly Disagree	Strongly Disagree
1. I can easily tell if someone else wants to enter a conversation.	☐	☐	☐	☐
2. I prefer animals to humans.	☐	☐	☐	☐
3. I try to keep up with the current trends and fashions.	☐	☐	☐	☐
4. I find it difficult to explain to others things that I understand easily, when they don't understand it the first time.	☐	☐	☐	☐
5. I dream most nights.	☐	☐	☐	☐
6. I really enjoy caring for other people.	☐	☐	☐	☐
7. I try to solve my own problems rather than discussing them with others.	☐	☐	☐	☐
8. I find it hard to know what to do in a social situation.	☐	☐	☐	☐
9. I am at my best first thing in the morning.	☐	☐	☐	☐
10. People often tell me that I went too far in making my point in a discussion.	☐	☐	☐	☐
11. It doesn't bother me too much if I am late meeting a friend.	☐	☐	☐	☐
12. Friendships and relationships are just too difficult, so I tend not to bother with them.	☐	☐	☐	☐
13. I would never break a law, no matter how minor.	☐	☐	☐	☐
14. I often find it difficult to judge if someone is rude or polite.	☐	☐	☐	☐
15. In a conversation, I tend to focus on my own thoughts rather than on what my listener might be thinking.	☐	☐	☐	☐
16. I prefer practical jokes to verbal humor.	☐	☐	☐	☐
17. I live life for today rather than the future.	☐	☐	☐	☐
18. I can pick up quickly if someone says one thing but means another.	☐	☐	☐	☐
19. I can easily tell if someone else is interested or bored with what I am saying.	☐	☐	☐	☐
20. I get upset if I see people suffering on news programs.	☐	☐	☐	☐

Source: The Essential Difference: The Truth About the Male and Female Brain, by S. Baron-Cohen, 2003, New York: Basic Books. Copyright 2003 by Basic Books. Adapted with permission.

	Strongly Agree	Slightly Agree	Slightly Disagree	Strongly Disagree
21. Friends usually talk to me about their problems, as they say that I am very understanding.	☐	☐	☐	☐
22. I can sense if I am intruding, even if the other person doesn't tell me.	☐	☐	☐	☐
23. I often start new hobbies but quickly become bored with them and move on to something else.	☐	☐	☐	☐
24. People sometimes tell me that I have gone too far with teasing.	☐	☐	☐	☐
25. I would be too nervous to go on a big roller coaster.	☐	☐	☐	☐
26. Other people often say that I am insensitive, though I don't always see why.	☐	☐	☐	☐
27. If I see a stranger in a group, I think that it is up to them to make an effort to join in.	☐	☐	☐	☐
28. I usually stay emotionally detached when watching a film.	☐	☐	☐	☐
29. I like to be very organized in day-to-day life and often make lists of the chores I have to do.	☐	☐	☐	☐
30. I can tune in to how someone else feels rapidly and intuitively.	☐	☐	☐	☐
31. I don't like to take risks.	☐	☐	☐	☐
32. I can easily determine what another person might want to talk about.	☐	☐	☐	☐
33. I can tell if someone is masking their true emotion.	☐	☐	☐	☐
34. Before making a decision, I always weigh the pros and cons.	☐	☐	☐	☐
35. I don't consciously work out the rules of social situations.	☐	☐	☐	☐
36. I am good at predicting what someone will do.	☐	☐	☐	☐
37. I tend to get emotionally involved with a friend's problems.	☐	☐	☐	☐
38. I can usually appreciate the other person's viewpoint, even if I don't agree with it.	☐	☐	☐	☐

Source: *The Essential Difference: The Truth About the Male and Female Brain,* by S. Baron-Cohen, 2003, New York: Basic Books. Copyright 2003 by Basic Books. Adapted with permission,

Name _____   Date _____

I Feel Stressed

I feel stressed when . . .

Agree	Disagree	
❏	❏	My parents are really upset with me.
❏	❏	I have an argument with my best friend.
❏	❏	I don't have enough money for the things I would like.
❏	❏	I feel my appearance is not what I want it to be.

Agree	Disagree	
❏	❏	I have too much to do and not enough time to do it.
❏	❏	I don't know what to do in a given situation.
❏	❏	I loan money to friends who don't repay it.
❏	❏	A friend tells a shared secret to others or betrays me.

How does stress affect you?

Stress affects me physically.

Agree	Disagree	
❏	❏	My muscles get tense.
❏	❏	My hands get cold or sweaty.
❏	❏	My stomach feels as if it is churning.
❏	❏	I have difficulty sleeping.
❏	❏	My heart beats rapidly.
❏	❏	I have sudden bursts of energy.
❏	❏	I am extremely tired.
❏	❏	I lose my appetite or eat too much.

Stress affects me emotionally.

Agree	Disagree	
❏	❏	I get nervous.
❏	❏	I cry or want to hit something.
❏	❏	I feel sad or giggle a lot.
❏	❏	I worry excessively.
❏	❏	I am irritable or feel depressed.

Agree	Disagree	
❏	❏	I feel bad about myself.
❏	❏	I daydream a lot at school.
❏	❏	I have bad dreams at night.
❏	❏	I get angry easily.
❏	❏	I lose interest in my appearance.

Stress affects my behavior.

Agree	Disagree	
❏	❏	I have difficulty concentrating.
❏	❏	I use food, drugs, or alcohol as a way to cope.
❏	❏	I use attention-getting antics.
❏	❏	I become grouchy or sarcastic.
❏	❏	I become abrasive or get into fights.
❏	❏	I may not tell the truth about something.
❏	❏	I get into arguments or fights with others.
❏	❏	I deliberately do poor-quality work.

Source: You & Self-Esteem: The Key to Happiness & Success (pp. 57–58), by B. Youngs, 1992, Austin, TX: PRO-ED. Copyright 1992 by PRO-ED, Inc. Adapted with permission.

Name _____   Date _____

Support Network Scale

☀ **Circle one response (number) for each item. Then, add the numbers you circled and put the total in the box.**

▣ How many persons do you talk to about a school/work problem?

   0 none

   3 one

   4 two or three

   5 four or more

▣ How many friends do you trade favors with, such as loan items, share meals, or help with tasks?

   0 none

   3 one

   4 two or three

   5 four or more

▣ Do you have a close friend or best friend?

   0 no

   2 several different friends

   6 one steady friend

   10 many friends, one best friend

▣ How often do friends and close family members visit you at home?

   0 rarely

   1 about once a month

   4 several times a month

   8 once a week or more

▣ How many friends or family members do you talk to about personal matters?

   0 none

   6 one or two

   8 three to five

   10 six or more

▣ How often do you participate in a social, community, or sports group?

   0 rarely

   1 about once a month

   2 once a week or more

Total

If your total network support score is . . .

Less than 10: Your support network has low strength and probably does not provide much support. You need to consider getting closer to people.

15–29: Your support network has moderate strength and likely provides enough support except during periods of high stress.

30 or more: Your support network has high strength, and it will probably maintain your well-being even during periods of high stress.

Source: Belonging (p. 244), by J. Devencenzi and S. Pendergast, 1999, Austin, TX: PRO-ED. Copyright 1999 by PRO-ED, Inc. Adapted with permission.

Name _____   Date _____

Behavior Checklist

Person completing the form _____

☼ **Rate each of the listed behaviors according to how well it describes this student.**

         1 = **Not at all**   2 = **Moderately well**   3 = **Very well**

1. Is pleased with his or her own accomplishments	1	2	3
2. Knows his or her own strengths and weaknesses	1	2	3
3. Expresses needs and feelings appropriately	1	2	3
4. Is comfortable giving and receiving affection	1	2	3
5. Is well-behaved	1	2	3
6. Is well-liked by peers	1	2	3
7. Thinks before speaking or acting	1	2	3
8. Approaches new experiences confidently	1	2	3
9. Expresses opinions well	1	2	3
10. Accepts criticism well	1	2	3
11. Is a good listener	1	2	3
12. Can accept things not going his or her own way	1	2	3
13. Adjusts well to changes	1	2	3
14. Makes friends easily	1	2	3
15. Resolves his or her own peer problems effectively	1	2	3

Please describe any other pertinent behavior.

_____

_____

_____

_____

Source: Belonging (p. 26), by J. Devencenzi and S. Pendergast, 1999, Austin, TX: PRO-ED. Copyright 1999 by PRO-ED, Inc. Adapted with permission.

Name _____   Date _____

Social Skills

☼ **Check the column that best fits your skills.**

Personal Interaction With Others

	Adequate	Needs Work	Unsatisfactory
1. Speaks in appropriate tone of voice	☐	☐	☐
2. Makes eye contact	☐	☐	☐
3. Expresses positive attitude	☐	☐	☐
4. Shows anger appropriately	☐	☐	☐
5. Accepts responsibility for actions	☐	☐	☐
6. Uses appropriate table manners	☐	☐	☐
7. Personal hygiene is acceptable	☐	☐	☐
8. Dresses appropriately	☐	☐	☐
9. Shows affection appropriately	☐	☐	☐
10. States disagreement appropriately	☐	☐	☐
11. Willing to accept a compromise	☐	☐	☐
12. Tells the truth	☐	☐	☐
13. Respects the property of others	☐	☐	☐

Initiates Interaction With Others

	Adequate	Needs Work	Unsatisfactory
14. Initiates conversation appropriately	☐	☐	☐
15. Volunteers to help others	☐	☐	☐
16. Makes appropriate greetings	☐	☐	☐
17. Avoids inappropriate physical contact	☐	☐	☐
18. Seeks attention appropriately	☐	☐	☐
19. Gives compliments to others	☐	☐	☐
20. Makes complaints appropriately	☐	☐	☐
21. When wrong, initiates apology	☐	☐	☐
22. Able to introduce self to others	☐	☐	☐

➥

Source: Putting the Pieces Together (pp. 26a–26c), by Area Education Agency 7, n.d. Adapted with permission.

Responses to Social Contacts

	Adequate	Needs Work	Unsatisfactory
23. Respects personal space of others	☐	☐	☐
24. Makes appropriate comments	☐	☐	☐
25. Avoids inappropriate gestures	☐	☐	☐
26. Takes turns in conversation	☐	☐	☐
27. Responds appropriately to teasing	☐	☐	☐
28. Manages frustration appropriately	☐	☐	☐
29. Responds appropriately to criticism	☐	☐	☐
30. Responds appropriately to praise	☐	☐	☐
31. Responds appropriately to authority	☐	☐	☐
32. Attends during instruction	☐	☐	☐
33. Follows verbal directions	☐	☐	☐
34. Follows written directions	☐	☐	☐
35. Remains on-task	☐	☐	☐
36. Able to verbalize instructions given	☐	☐	☐
37. Ignores distractions	☐	☐	☐
38. Recognizes informal social rules	☐	☐	☐
39. Acknowledges greetings from others	☐	☐	☐
40. Participates in group activities	☐	☐	☐
41. Works independently	☐	☐	☐
42. Resists peer pressure	☐	☐	☐
43. Makes refusals appropriately	☐	☐	☐
44. Accepts "no" for an answer	☐	☐	☐
45. Responds appropriately to an angry person	☐	☐	☐

Source: Putting the Pieces Together (pp. 26a–26c), by Area Education Agency 7, n.d. Adapted with permission.

Name _____   Date _____

Social-Emotional Skills Student Form

☀ **Write a 1, 2, or 3 on the line in front of each statement to show your level of skill.**

1 = Almost never   2 = Sometimes   3 = Almost always

Social-Emotional Skill

_____ **Using Body Language**—I know which body actions and facial expressions to use to show my feelings.

_____ **Using Manners**—I use appropriate manners (for example, saying "Please" and "Thank you" and using polite table manners).

_____ **Choosing the Right Time and Place**—My comments deal with the main topic when I have a conversation. I warn others before I switch topics.

_____ **Staying On and Switching Topics**—My comments deal with the main topic when I have a conversation. I warn others before I switch topics.

_____ **Listening**—When someone is talking to me, I give that person my full attention.

_____ **Conversing**—I feel comfortable starting conversations. I begin with a greeting and my name. I end conversations smoothly.

_____ **Making a Positive First Impression**—I try to make a positive impression by how I look, what I say, and what I do when I meet new people.

_____ **Using Formal and Informal Language**—When I speak to people in respected positions, I talk in a more "traditional" way. When I speak to people my own age or adults I feel close to, I talk in a more "relaxed" way.

_____ **Giving Reasons**—When someone asks me to explain something, I give reasons that are specific and relevant.

_____ **Planning What To Say**—I think about what I am going to say before I speak.

_____ **Interrupting**—I only interrupt people when it is necessary. I interrupt others appropriately.

_____ **Giving a Compliment**—I give people compliments about the way they look, the items they own, and what they say and do. I don't give compliments just to get people to like me.

_____ **Accepting a Compliment**—When someone gives me a compliment, I say "thank you" in a sincere way.

_____ **Saying "Thank You"**—I thank people when they do something nice for me.

_____ **Introducing Yourself**—I introduce myself to people I don't know. I remember to tell my full name.

_____ **Introducing People**—I introduce people when they do not know each other (for example, "Steve, meet Beth. Beth, this is Steve").

_____ **Making a Request**—When I want something, I ask for it in a polite way. I do not demand things from others.

_____ **Offering Help**—I offer help to people in need. I ask first instead of just taking over right away.

_____ **Asking for Help**—I try things on my own first. If I can't figure something out, I ask for help in an appropriate way.

_____ **Asking for Permission**—I ask for permission from authority figures whenever I should.

_____ **Accepting "No"**—I act mature when I am told "no" by an authority figure.

➡

Source: Social Skills Strategies: A Social-Emotional Curriculum for Adolescents (2nd ed., pp. 380–384), by N. Gajewski, P. Mayo, and P. Hirn, 1998, Eau Claire, WI: Thinking Publications. Copyright 1998 by Thinking Publications. Adapted with permission.

1 = Almost never   2 = Sometimes   3 = Almost always

_____ **Making an Apology**—I say "I'm sorry" when I have done something wrong.

_____ **Expressing an Opinion**—When I say something that is just my opinion, I remember to begin with statements like "I think . . ." or "In my opinion . . . ."

_____ **Agreeing or Disagreeing**—When I disagree with others, I do not put down their ideas or opinions. I do not get angry when others disagree with me.

_____ **Convincing Others**—I give good reasons when I try to convince someone to agree with me.

_____ **Giving Information**—I express myself clearly when I give information to others (for example, giving directions, answering questions).

_____ **Dealing With Contradictions**—When I hear a contradiction (statements that are opposite in meaning), I ask what is meant.

_____ **Being Honest**—I am truthful, even when I have done something wrong. I don't want to lose people's trust in me.

_____ **Being Optimistic**—I try to have a positive attitude. I expect good things to happen. I look on the bright side when something goes wrong.

_____ **Having a Positive Reputation**—I have a positive reputation at home, at school, and in the community.

_____ **Starting a Friendship**—I am good at starting new friendships with others.

_____ **Maintaining a Friendship**—I keep my friends because I treat them well.

_____ **Giving Emotional Support**—When one of my friends is feeling depressed or having a problem, I listen and give encouragement.

_____ **Giving Advice**—I only give advice when someone asks me to do so. I avoid giving advice about things I don't know much about.

_____ **Ignoring**—I ignore disruptions. I ignore others who try to get my attention in a negative way.

_____ **Dealing With Teasing**—I laugh when people tease me in a friendly way. I ignore people when they tease me in a mean way.

_____ **Dealing With Peer Pressure**—I say "no" when others try to pressure me into doing thing I don't feel comfortable doing.

_____ **Joining In**—I feel comfortable joining conversations and activities after they have already begun. I join others in a way that is not disruptive.

_____ **Dealing With Being Left Out**—When I am left out of an activity or a conversation, I try to decide if it happened by mistake or on purpose. If it seems like a mistake, I try to join the activity without being disruptive. If it seems like others purposely excluded me, I find something else to do.

_____ **Telling On Others**—I only tell on others for important reasons. When I do tell on others, I only tell the person who needs to know about the behavior.

_____ **Being Assertive**—When someone goes against my rights, I tell the other person how I feel and what I want. I do not make threats or get aggressive.

_____ **Making a Complaint**—I only make complaints when it is fair to do so. I do not become aggressive when I make a complaint.

_____ **Receiving a Complaint**—When someone complains to me, and I know I am responsible, I apologize and offer a solution.

Source: Social Skills Strategies: A Social-Emotional Curriculum for Adolescents (2nd ed., pp. 380–384), by N. Gajewski, P. Mayo, and P. Hirn, 1998, Eau Claire, WI: Thinking Publications. Copyright 1998 by Thinking Publications. Adapted with permission.

1 = Almost never   2 = Sometimes   3 = Almost always

_____ **Giving Constructive Criticism**—When I criticize others, I tell exactly what I think should be improved. I do not personally insult the other person. I try to say something positive about the person first.

_____ **Accepting Constructive Criticism**—I can handle it when someone tells me I need to improve on something. I don't get defensive.

_____ **Making an Accusation**—I make sure I have proof before I accuse someone of doing something wrong.

_____ **Dealing With a False Accusation**—When someone accuses me of doing something wrong and I didn't do it, I stay calm. I offer proof that I am innocent or try to offer another explanation.

_____ **Negotiating and Compromising**—I am willing to give in a little to help solve a disagreement. I don't always need things to go my way.

_____ **Accepting Consequences**—When I know I have done something wrong, I am willing to face the consequence.

_____ **Expressing Feelings**—I talk about my feelings when it's appropriate.

_____ **Dealing With Anger**—When I feel angry, I can control myself. I don't lose control.

_____ **Dealing With Embarrassment**—I handle myself well when I get embarrassed. I don't fall apart.

_____ **Coping With Fear**—When I am afraid of something, I don't let it control me. I face my fears and try to reduce them.

_____ **Dealing With Failure**—I don't let myself get "down" when I fail at something, I just try to do better the next time.

_____ **Dealing With Disappointment**—I stay in control when I am disappointed because someone or something lets me down.

_____ **Understanding the Feelings of Others**—I am sensitive to the way other people are feeling.

Write the social-emotional skills you think you most need to improve.

❶ _____

❷ _____

❸ _____

Source: Social Skills Strategies: A Social-Emotional Curriculum for Adolescents (2nd ed., pp. 380–384), by N. Gajewski, P. Mayo, and P. Hirn, 1998, Eau Claire, WI: Thinking Publications. Copyright 1998 by Thinking Publications. Adapted with permission.

Daily Living

List of Inventories

Name _____ Date _____

Ansell-Casey Life Skills Assessment

	Not Like Me	Somewhat Like Me	Very Much Like Me

Daily Living

	Not Like Me	Somewhat Like Me	Very Much Like Me
1. I plan nutritious meals.	1	2	3
2. I evaluate my diet for nutritional balance.	1	2	3
3. I eat a variety of healthy foods each day.	1	2	3
4. I think about how what I eat impacts my health.	1	2	3
5. I look at calories and fat content on product labels.	1	2	3
6. I eat some vegetables each day.	1	2	3
7. I use a shopping list at the grocery store.	1	2	3
8. I compare prices to get the best value.	1	2	3
9. I clean kitchen equipment after meal preparation.	1	2	3
10. I can make meals using a recipe.	1	2	3
11. I follow the directions on cleaning products.	1	2	3
12. I check clothing-care directions when doing laundry.	1	2	3
13. I use good table manners.	1	2	3

Housing and Money Management

	Not Like Me	Somewhat Like Me	Very Much Like Me
1. I can calculate the costs of car ownership (e.g., registration, maintenance).	1	2	3
2. I can describe how to monitor a checking-account balance.	1	2	3
3. I can describe how to develop a good credit rating.	1	2	3
4. I can name three disadvantages of purchasing with credit.	1	2	3
5. I know the typical fee charged for ATM transactions.	1	2	3
6. I understand what is covered by liability car insurance.	1	2	3
7. I know where to find tax information on a pay stub.	1	2	3
8. I know how to find out about my credit rating.	1	2	3
9. I can calculate housing start-up costs (e.g., application fee, security deposit).	1	2	3
10. I know where in my community one can get help for completing tax returns.	1	2	3
11. I know the advantages and disadvantages of buying from "rent-to-own" stores.	1	2	3
12. I know what information is asked for in an apartment rental application.	1	2	3
13. I balance my bank statement regularly.	1	2	3
14. I can use an Automatic Teller Machine (ATM).	1	2	3
15. I understand the consequences of breaking a lease.	1	2	3

Source: Ansell-Casey Life Skills Assessment, Youth Level 4 (pp. 1–13), by Casey Family Programs and D. I. Ansell, 2000. Retrieved February 2006 from www.caseylifeskills.org. Copyright 2000 by Casey Family Programs and D. I. Ansell. Adapted with permission.

	Not Like Me	Somewhat Like Me	Very Much Like Me
16. I can explain the benefits of having homeowner's or renter's insurance.	1	2	3
17. I have completed an income tax form.	1	2	3
18. I plan for the expenses that I must pay each month.	1	2	3
19. I can name two ways to invest money.	1	2	3
20. I can identify two ways to put money into savings.	1	2	3
21. I keep a record when I pay bills.	1	2	3
22. I can complete a money order.	1	2	3
23. I can get to an appointment by myself, even if I have not been to that location before.	1	2	3
24. I can describe two or more ways to search for housing.	1	2	3
25. I know the necessary steps for getting a driver's license.	1	2	3
26. I can compare housing choices based on cleanliness and costs.	1	2	3
27. I have developed a budget.	1	2	3
28. I compute discounts; for example, how much a $12.90 item would cost after a 15% discount.	1	2	3
29. I know the consequences of driving without insurance.	1	2	3

Self Care

	Not Like Me	Somewhat Like Me	Very Much Like Me
1. I can identify two signs of pregnancy.	1	2	3
2. I can identify two community resources that provide prenatal care.	1	2	3
3. I can identify two ways to avoid peer pressure to use drugs.	1	2	3
4. I can identify three methods of birth control.	1	2	3
5. I can explain ways to protect myself from sexually transmitted diseases (STDs).	1	2	3
6. I know how to talk to a partner about sexually transmitted diseases (STDs). . . .	1	2	3
7. I can describe two strategies for responsible drinking.	1	2	3
8. I can explain what to do when a fever doesn't improve.	1	2	3
9. I can resist pressure to have sex.	1	2	3
10. I can explain how hygiene affects one's health.	1	2	3
11. I can explain when it is best to make a doctor's appointment instead of visiting the emergency room.	1	2	3
12. I know how to make a dental appointment.	1	2	3
13. If illegal drugs are offered to me, I can refuse them.	1	2	3
14. I treat simple injuries like cuts, bites, stings, and splinters.	1	2	3
15. I know where I could go to get help with depression or other emotional problems.	1	2	3

Source: Ansell-Casey Life Skills Assessment, Youth Level 4 (pp. 1–13), by Casey Family Programs and D. I. Ansell, 2000. Retrieved February 2006 from www.caseylifeskills.org. Copyright 2000 by Casey Family Programs and D. I. Ansell. Adapted with permission.

Social Relationships

	Not Like Me	Somewhat Like Me	Very Much Like Me
1. I confide in my friends.	1	2	3
2. I turn to others for support when I have family problems.	1	2	3
3. I am part of a group, besides my family, that cares about me.	1	2	3
4. I show others that I care about them.	1	2	3
5. I encourage others to talk about their feelings.	1	2	3
6. I am comfortable with the number of friends I have.	1	2	3
7. I can identify two or more people I can turn to for help.	1	2	3
8. I usually receive feedback without getting angry.	1	2	3

Extra Items

	Not Like Me	Somewhat Like Me	Very Much Like Me
1. I know where a fire extinguisher is located where I live.	1	2	3
2. I know the rights and responsibilities of a tenant.	1	2	3
3. I know how to get emergency assistance to pay utilities.	1	2	3
4. I know who to contact to get low-income housing.	1	2	3
5. I know where in my area I can go to access the Internet.	1	2	3
6. I can explain the benefits of doing volunteer work.	1	2	3
7. I can use resources other than the newspaper to find job openings.	1	2	3
8. I have written my résumé.	1	2	3
9. I know where the nearest state employment office is located.	1	2	3
10. I know how to use a computer.	1	2	3
11. I understand what is included in employee benefits.	1	2	3

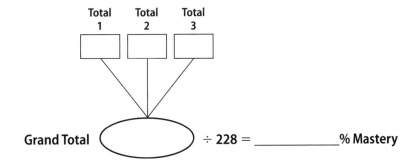

Total 1   Total 2   Total 3

Grand Total ÷ 228 = _____ **% Mastery**

Source: Ansell-Casey Life Skills Assessment, Youth Level 4 (pp. 1–13), by Casey Family Programs and D. I. Ansell, 2000. Retrieved February 2006 from www.caseylifeskills.org. Copyright 2000 by Casey Family Programs and D. I. Ansell. Adapted with permission.

Name _____   Date _____

Transition Activities for Daily Living

Person completing the form: ❑ Student   ❑ Parent   ❑ Teacher

☼ Rate the importance of each instructional activity for the student's future by choosing the appropriate number. These activities can be used to develop instructional objectives on the IEP.

Consider	In Progress	Completed	
1	2	3	Develop personal-care skills including hygiene, health, and private and public behavior.
1	2	3	Develop acceptable intimate/sexual behavior.
1	2	3	Develop housekeeping and cooking skills.
1	2	3	Develop budgeting skills.
1	2	3	Identify who to call and what to do in emergency situations.
1	2	3	Participate in an independent living training program.
1	2	3	Identify persons or services to assist in locating a place to live.
1	2	3	Apply for case management services, if applicable.
1	2	3	Identify neighborhood services and supports.
1	2	3	Identify and apply for financial support (i.e., SSI).
1	2	3	Identify resources and support for child care, if necessary.
1	2	3	Identify transportation services near home.
1	2	3	Other _____
1	2	3	Other _____

What are the skills needed by the student in this area?

_____

_____

_____

_____

Name _____   Date _____

Home Living

☀ **Mark your level of interest and the amount of support you will need to get the kind of home living you want.**

Interest Level				Support Needed			
Not Interested	Interested	Very Interested		None	Minimum	Moderate	Maximum
☐	☐	☐	Live alone or independently	☐	☐	☐	☐
☐	☐	☐	Live with friends or roommates	☐	☐	☐	☐
☐	☐	☐	Live with parents or foster parents	☐	☐	☐	☐
☐	☐	☐	Live with other relatives	☐	☐	☐	☐
☐	☐	☐	Live with husband or wife	☐	☐	☐	☐
☐	☐	☐	Live in supervised setting	☐	☐	☐	☐
☐	☐	☐	Manage personal finances	☐	☐	☐	☐
☐	☐	☐	Get around the community	☐	☐	☐	☐
☐	☐	☐	Care for personal needs	☐	☐	☐	☐
☐	☐	☐	Select/manage a household	☐	☐	☐	☐
☐	☐	☐	Buy/prepare food	☐	☐	☐	☐
☐	☐	☐	Make adequate decisions	☐	☐	☐	☐

Goals or Activities I Would Like To Do for Home Living

◾ _____

◾ _____

◾ _____

Source: Transition Skills Assessment (pp. 3–4), by Minnesota Interagency Office on Transition Services, 1996, St. Paul, MN: Author. Copyright 1996 by Minnesota Interagency Office on Transition Services. Adapted with permission.

Name _____   Date _____

Daily Living Skills Competency Rating

Person completing the form: ❏ Student   ❏ Parent   ❏ Teacher

☀ Rate the student's mastery of each item using the rating key below. Use the NR rating for items which cannot be rated. For subcompetencies rated 0 or 1, place a check mark in the appropriate space in the Yes or No column to indicate ability to perform the subcompetency with assistance.

0 = Not competent	1 = Partially competent	2 = Competent	NR = Not rated

	Rating	With Assistance	
		Yes	No

Managing Personal Finances

	Rating	Yes	No
1. Identify money and make correct change........................	☐	☐	☐
2. Make responsible expenditures................................	☐	☐	☐
3. Keep basic financial records	☐	☐	☐
4. Calculate and pay taxes	☐	☐	☐
5. Use credit responsibly.......................................	☐	☐	☐
6. Use banking services..	☐	☐	☐

Selecting and Managing a Household

	Rating	Yes	No
1. Maintain home exterior/interior	☐	☐	☐
2. Use basic appliances and tools	☐	☐	☐
3. Select adequate housing.....................................	☐	☐	☐
4. Set up household..	☐	☐	☐
5. Maintain home grounds	☐	☐	☐

Caring for Personal Needs

	Rating	Yes	No
1. Demonstrate knowledge of physical fitness, nutrition, and weight	☐	☐	☐
2. Exhibit proper grooming and hygiene	☐	☐	☐
3. Dress appropriately	☐	☐	☐
4. Demonstrate knowledge of common illness, prevention, and treatment...........	☐	☐	☐
5. Practice personal safety	☐	☐	☐

Raising Children and Meeting Marriage Responsibilities

	Rating	Yes	No
1. Demonstrate physical care for raising children..................	☐	☐	☐
2. Know psychological aspects of raising children.................	☐	☐	☐
3. Demonstrate marriage responsibilities........................	☐	☐	☐

Source: Life Centered Career Education: A Competency-Based Approach (4th ed., pp. 194–195), by D. Brolin, 1993, Reston, VA: The Council for Exceptional Children. Copyright 1993 by the Council for Exceptional Children. Adapted with permission.

70 ◈ *Daily Living*

© 2008 by PRO-ED, Inc.

	Rating	With Assistance	
		Yes	No

Buying, Preparing, and Consuming Food

	Rating	Yes	No
1. Purchase food	☐	☐	☐
2. Clean food preparation areas	☐	☐	☐
3. Store food	☐	☐	☐
4. Prepare meals	☐	☐	☐
5. Demonstrate appropriate eating habits	☐	☐	☐
6. Plan and eat balanced meals	☐	☐	☐

Buying and Caring for Clothing

	Rating	Yes	No
1. Wash/clean clothing	☐	☐	☐
2. Purchase clothing	☐	☐	☐
3. Iron, mend, and store clothing	☐	☐	☐

Exhibiting Responsible Citizenship

	Rating	Yes	No
1. Demonstrate knowledge of civil rights and responsibilities	☐	☐	☐
2. Demonstrate knowledge of local, state, and federal governments	☐	☐	☐
3. Demonstrate knowledge of the law and ability to follow the law	☐	☐	☐
4. Demonstrate knowledge of citizens' rights and responsibilities	☐	☐	☐

Using Recreational Facilities and Engaging in Leisure Activities

	Rating	Yes	No
1. Demonstrate knowledge of available community resources	☐	☐	☐
2. Choose and plan activities	☐	☐	☐
3. Demonstrate knowledge of the value of recreation	☐	☐	☐
4. Engage in group and individual activities	☐	☐	☐
5. Plan vacation time	☐	☐	☐

Getting Around the Community

	Rating	Yes	No
1. Demonstrate knowledge of traffic rules and safety	☐	☐	☐
2. Demonstrate knowledge and use of various means of transportation	☐	☐	☐
3. Find way around the community	☐	☐	☐
4. Drive a car	☐	☐	☐

Source: Life Centered Career Education: A Competency-Based Approach (4th ed., pp. 194–195), by D. Brolin, 1993, Reston, VA: The Council for Exceptional Children. Copyright 1993 by the Council for Exceptional Children. Adapted with permission.

Name _____   Date _____

Living Skills Checklist

Person completing the form _____

A = Asset   U = Unknown   L = Limitation

Personal Hygiene/Grooming

____ **1.** Washes hands

____ **2.** Washes hair

____ **3.** Washes body

____ **4.** Uses deodorant

____ **5.** Combs/brushes hair

____ **6.** Brushes teeth

____ **7.** Shaves using razor (electric or manual)

____ **8.** Cleans/clips fingernails and toenails

____ **9.** *(Female)* Handles feminine hygiene

____ **10.** Uses tissue/handkerchief

____ **11.** Wears clean clothes

____ **12.** Wears clothes that fit and are in good repair

Housekeeping

____ **1.** Sweeps floor

____ **2.** Mops floor

____ **3.** Cleans bathroom

____ **4.** Washes dishes

____   **a.** Uses sink

____   **b.** Uses dishwasher

____ **5.** Dries dishes

____ **6.** Stores dishes/pans/utensils in proper place

____ **7.** Cleans counter/table

____ **8.** Disposes of garbage in garbage disposal or garbage container

Laundry/Clothing Care

____ **1.** Sorts clothes (light/white, dark/colored)

____ **2.** Uses regular washer

____ **3.** Uses regular dryer

____ **4.** Folds/hangs clothes

____ **5.** Mends clothes (buttons, hems, seams)

Time

____ **1.** Distinguishes units of time

____   **a.** day/night

____   **b.** morning/evening/afternoon

____ **2.** Distinguishes a.m./p.m.

____ **3.** Distinguishes workdays/nonworkdays

____ **4.** Tells time by hour and half hour

____ **5.** Sets/uses alarm clock

____ **6.** Arrives on time

____ **7.** Identifies date: day, month, year

____ **8.** Identifies numbers of days in week

____ **9.** Uses calendar

____ **10.** Estimates amount of time to do task

____   **a.** cleaning

____   **b.** shopping

____   **c.** cooking

____   **d.** leisure activity

____   **e.** shower/bath

____   **f.** walk to mall

Numbers

____ **1.** Recognizes numerals

____   **a.** 0 to 12

____   **b.** above 12

Source: Transdisciplinary Vocational Assessment: Issues in School-Based Programs (pp. 389–393), by E. M. Levinson, 1993, Brandon, VT: Clinical Psychology Publishing. Copyright 1993 by Clinical Psychology Publishing Co., Inc. Adapted with permission.

___ **2.** Copies numerals:

___   **a.** 0 to 12

___   **b.** above 12

___ **3.** Counts objects:

___   **a.** 0 to 12

___   **b.** above 12

___ **4.** Uses calculator to add, subtract, multiply, divide

___ **5.** Uses measuring cups and spoons

___ **6.** Uses a ruler and tape measure

Writing

___ **1.** Writes/copies full name in manuscript or cursive

___ **2.** Writes/copies

___   **a.** Address

___   **b.** Social Security number

___   **c.** Telephone number

___   **d.** Date of birth

___ **3.** Writes/copies sentences/letters

___ **4.** Addresses envelope

___ **5.** Mails letters

___ **6.** Fills out job application

Money

___ **1.** Gives correct coin amounts for

___   **a.** 10 cents

___   **b.** 30 cents

___   **c.** 75 cents

___ **2.** Uses coins/bill combinations for

___   **a.** 1 dollar

___   **b.** 5 dollars

___   **c.** 10 dollars

___ **3.** Uses concept of "more than" / "less than"

___ **4.** Estimates cost of purchase

___ **5.** Uses checkbook

___ **6.** Carries own money/Performs cash transactions/ Waits for change if necessary

Reading

___ **1.** Reads own name

___ **2.** Reads important signs/functional words

___ **3.** Reads newspaper:

___   **a.** locates want ads

___   **b.** uses want ads to find job

Personal/Social Skills

___ **1.** Carries identification (ID)

___ **2.** Responds when spoken to

___ **3.** Communicates basic needs: verbally, nonverbally

___ **4.** Communicates full name: verbally, using ID, written

___ **5.** Communicates address, phone number: verbally, using ID, written

___ **6.** Communicates school or place of work: verbally, using ID, written

___ **7.** Uses others' names when interacting

___ **8.** Uses "please," "thank you," etc.

___ **9.** Expresses anger in acceptable manner

___ **10.** Expresses fear in acceptable manner

___ **11.** Expresses affection in acceptable manner: same sex, opposite sex

___ **12.** Expresses dislike in acceptable manner

___ **13.** Apologizes

___ **14.** Initiates interactions with

___   **a.** staff

___   **b.** peers

___   **c.** visitors

___   **d.** sales persons/waitresses

___ **15.** Converses with

___   **a.** staff

___   **b.** peers

___   **c.** visitors

___ **16.** Refrains from talking to strangers unless necessary

Source: Transdisciplinary Vocational Assessment: Issues in School-Based Programs (pp. 389–393), by E. M. Levinson, 1993, Brandon, VT: Clinical Psychology Publishing. Copyright 1993 by Clinical Psychology Publishing Co., Inc. Adapted with permission.

A = Asset   U = Unknown   L = Limitation

___ 17. Uses telephone

___   a. calls others

___   b. receives calls

___ 18. Answers door in acceptable manner

___ 19. Practices acceptable manners at

___   a. restaurant

___   b. theater/spectator event

___   c. party/dance

___   d. church

___   e. doctor

___   f. dentist

___ 20. Practices acceptable manners as

___   a. customer

___   b. guest

___   c. host

___ 21. Demonstrates a cooperative attitude

___   a. follows directions from staff

___   b. follows activity schedule

___   c. performs duties

___   d. works on training objectives

___ 22. Demonstrates trustworthiness

___   a. conduct can be trusted in unsupervised situations

___   b. tells the truth

___   c. takes responsibility for personal actions and decisions

___   d. asks permission to use others' possessions

___ 23. Accepts/adjusts to situations that are contrary to own will or desire

___ 24. Abides by group decisions

___ 25. Accepts/adjusts to staff changes

___ 26. Accepts/adjusts to novel situations: visitors, schedule changes

___ 27. Uses acceptable table manners

___ 28. Engages in a passive activity: TV, radio, stereo, movie

___ 29. Engages in solitary games

___ 30. Engages in games with others

___ 31. Engages in hobby/craft activity

___ 32. Engages in active socialization with friends, family, groups, parties, members of the opposite sex, social clubs

Food Preparation/Cooking

___ 1. Identifies kitchen utensils/cookware: table knife, spoon, fork, can opener, turner/spatula, sharp knife, measuring cup/spoons, scraper, soup ladle, pot holder/mitt, hot pad, napkin, cheese slicer, fry pan, saucepan, broiler pan, cake pan, pizza pan, cookie sheet, toaster

___ 2. Identifies dishes: plate, cereal bowl, soup bowl, mixing bowl, glass, cup, saucer, salt/pepper shaker, sugar bowl, platter

___ 3. Identifies appliances, etc.: stove, oven, refrigerator, dishwasher, cupboard, table, chair, sink, freezer

Mobility

___ 1. Walks

___ 2. Rides bicycle

___ 3. Rides city bus

___ 4. Rides bus to another city

___ 5. Gets to nearest

___   a. grocery store

___   b. laundromat

___   c. bus stop

___   d. shopping mall

___   e. church

___   f. doctor/dentist office

___   g. parental home

___   h. friend's home

___ 6. Identifies/reads street signs

___ 7. Identifies/reads house numbers

___ 8. Identifies appropriate places to go if lost: gas station, business place, home of another

Source: Transdisciplinary Vocational Assessment: Issues in School-Based Programs (pp. 389–393), by E. M. Levinson, 1993, Brandon, VT: Clinical Psychology Publishing. Copyright 1993 by Clinical Psychology Publishing Co., Inc. Adapted with permission.

Health/Safety

____ **1.** Treats simple health problems:

____   **a.** cuts/scrapes

____   **b.** slivers/splinters

____   **c.** upset stomach

____   **d.** cold

____ **2.** Contacts another for health problems more difficult to handle:

____   **a.** fever

____   **b.** diarrhea

____   **c.** burn

____   **d.** fainting spell

____   **e.** seizure

____   **f.** eye problems

____   **g.** poisoning/overdose

____   **h.** animal bite

____ **3.** Takes medication

____ **4.** Refills prescription

____ **5.** Reports/handles seizures

____ **6.** Uses telephone to call in sick

____ **7.** Avoids combining alcohol and medication

____ **8.** Has basic understanding of human sexuality/ sex education

____ **9.** Follows fire-drill instructions

____ **10.** Follows other disaster instructions

____ **11.** Wears safety goggles when operating power tools

Source: Transdisciplinary Vocational Assessment: Issues in School-Based Programs (pp. 389–393), by E. M. Levinson, 1993, Brandon, VT: Clinical Psychology Publishing. Copyright 1993 by Clinical Psychology Publishing Co., Inc. Adapted with permission.

Name _____   Date _____

Living on My Own

☀ **Circle your answer (Yes or No) to each question.**
Then put a ✓ in the box next to the questions you want to learn more about.

❑ **1.** Most people need a little help moving out on their own for the first time. Do I know someone I trust to help me set up a place to live? .... **Yes   No**

❑ **2.** Do I know where I will want to live? (Examples: apartment; house; mobile home; duplex; townhouse; dorm, if I go to a college or university).. **Yes   No**

❑ **3.** Do I know who I will want to live with? (Examples: by myself, with a friend or friends, with a relative, with a roommate that I don't already know, someone who is paid to help me with the things that are hard for me to do on my own) .... **Yes   No**

❑ **4.** Do I know how and where to look for a place to live? .... **Yes   No**

❑ **5.** Do I know how to fill out a housing application? .... **Yes   No**

❑ **6.** Do I know how to call and set up my phone, TV, and electricity for the first time? .... **Yes   No**

❑ **7.** Do I know how to get furniture? .... **Yes   No**

❑ **8.** Do I know how to do everyday chores like cooking, cleaning, and laundry? .... **Yes   No**

❑ **9.** Can I fix things around the house when they break, or do I know who to call? .... **Yes   No**

❑ **10.** Do I know how to use the air conditioner and heater? .... **Yes   No**

❑ **11.** Do I know how to use an alarm clock? .... **Yes   No**

❑ **12.** Do I know how to use a telephone book? .... **Yes   No**

❑ **13.** Do I know how to use a stove and oven? .... **Yes   No**

❑ **14.** Do I know how to use a microwave? .... **Yes   No**

❑ **15.** Do I know how to use a blender? .... **Yes   No**

❑ **16.** Do I know how to use a coffee maker? .... **Yes   No**

❑ **17.** Do I know how to use a dishwasher? .... **Yes   No**

❑ **18.** Do I know how to use a washer and dryer?... **Yes   No**

❑ **19.** Do I know how to use an iron? .... **Yes   No**

❑ **20.** Do I know how to use tools like a hammer, pliers, screwdriver, and wrench? .... **Yes   No**

Source: Adapted and used with permission of Julie Haffner.

How Do You Take Care of Your Clothes?

☀ **Your clothes will last longer and look better if you take care of them. What would you do if the following things happened?**

1. You are going to a dance, and the hem in your slacks/dress is coming out.

   _____

2. Your jacket/dress needs to be cleaned, and the tag reads "Dry Clean Only."

   _____

3. You broke the zipper in your pants.

   _____

4. You spilled ketchup on your tie/scarf when eating out with some friends.

   _____

5. The dress shirt/blouse you want to wear is really wrinkled.

   _____

6. As you take off your pants, you notice a grass/blood stain.

   _____

7. You want to wash your new pair of socks and not lose one.

   _____

8. There is a button missing on your favorite shirt.

   _____

9. The shoelace in one of your athletic shoes is unraveled, and you can't push it through the holes anymore to lace it up.

   _____

10. You notice there is a little rip in one of your shirts and a hole in the toe of your sock.

    _____

11. Your new red and white T-shirt is dirty. You are afraid to wash it because it might come out pink.

    _____

Source: Get A Life! Nothing Can Stop You Now! (pp. 13–17), 1994, Salt Lake City: Utah Independent Living Center. Copyright 1994 by Utah Independent Living Center. Adapted with permission.

Name _____   Date _____

Money

☀ **Circle your answer (Yes or No) to each question.**
Then put a ✓ in the box next to the questions you want to learn more about.

❑   **1.** A lot of people need help keeping track of their money at first. Do I know someone that I trust to help me with my money? .... **Yes   No**

❑   **2.** Do I know how to pay bills? .... **Yes   No**

❑   **3.** Do I know how to make and use a budget? .... **Yes   No**

❑   **4.** Do I know how to open and use a checking and savings account? .... **Yes   No**

❑   **5.** Do I know what I need to know about loans? .... **Yes   No**

❑   **6.** Do I know how to use an ATM? .... **Yes   No**

❑   **7.** Do I understand how a check works? .... **Yes   No**

❑   **8.** Do I know how to write a check? .... **Yes   No**

❑   **9.** Do I understand how a credit card works? .... **Yes   No**

❑   **10.** Do I know how to apply for and use a credit card? .... **Yes   No**

❑   **11.** Do I know what I need to know about debt? .... **Yes   No**

❑   **12.** Do I know how to make and count change? .... **Yes   No**

❑   **13.** Can I tell when I am being ripped off? .... **Yes   No**

❑   **14.** Do I understand contracts for cell phones and pagers? .... **Yes   No**

Source: Adapted and used with permission of Julie Haffner.

Name _____   Date _____

Money Management

☼ **If you could buy any three things in the whole world that you wanted, what would they be?**

	What I Would Buy	Why I Would Buy It
1.	_____	_____
2.	_____	_____
3.	_____	_____

☼ **Now, with the amount of money you know you can really get during the next year or so, what would you like to save for?**

	What I Would Save For	Why I Would Save For It
1.	_____	_____
2.	_____	_____
3.	_____	_____

☼ **What are your attitudes about money? Circle *Yes, Sometimes,* or *No* to show how much you agree with each statement.**

1. I try to earn money however I can.	Yes	Sometimes	No
2. I like to have money, but I don't like working to get it.	Yes	Sometimes	No
3. I like money just so I can look at it and see how much I have.	Yes	Sometimes	No
4. I like money for the things it can buy for me, more than for itself.	Yes	Sometimes	No
5. I think all the excitement about money is silly. Other things are more important to me.	Yes	Sometimes	No

☼ **You might have some other feelings about money. If so, list them below.**

_____

_____

_____

_____

Source: Life Skills for Teens (p. 66), by S. Palomares and D. Schilling, 1994, Austin, TX: PRO-ED. Copyright 1994 by PRO-ED, Inc. Adapted with permission.

Name _____   Date _____

What Is a Budget?

☼ **Each of the terms listed below has something to do with earning and spending money. Put a check mark in the box in the column that indicates the appropriate category.**

	Earned Income	Deductions from Income	Fixed Expenses	Flexible Expenses
1. Federal taxes	❑	❑	❑	❑
2. Overtime pay	❑	❑	❑	❑
3. Clothing	❑	❑	❑	❑
4. State taxes	❑	❑	❑	❑
5. Hourly wages	❑	❑	❑	❑
6. Car payment	❑	❑	❑	❑
7. Social Security	❑	❑	❑	❑
8. Phone bill	❑	❑	❑	❑
9. House payment	❑	❑	❑	❑
10. Money from gifts	❑	❑	❑	❑
11. Electric and water bill	❑	❑	❑	❑
12. Gas for car	❑	❑	❑	❑
13. Household expenses	❑	❑	❑	❑
14. Food	❑	❑	❑	❑
15. Recreation expenses	❑	❑	❑	❑
16. Union dues	❑	❑	❑	❑

Source: *Life Skills Activities for Secondary Students with Special Needs,* by D. Mannix, 1995, West Nyack, NY: The Center for Applied Research in Education. Copyright 1995 by The Center for Applied Research in Education. Adapted with permission.

Name _____ Date _____

Health Inventory

☼ **Circle one number for each statement.**

1 = Not true at all   2 = Mostly untrue   3 = Somewhat true   4 = Mostly true   5 = Perfect description

1 2 3 4 5   ▣ I eat a well-balanced diet. .... _____

1 2 3 4 5   ▣ My weight is about right for me. .... _____

1 2 3 4 5   ▣ I engage in a regular exercise program. .... _____

1 2 3 4 5   ▣ I have an abundance of energy. .... _____

1 2 3 4 5   ▣ I don't pay much attention to my physical development. .... _____

1 2 3 4 5   ▣ I have specific goals related to physical fitness. .... _____

1 2 3 4 5   ▣ I get adequate rest. .... _____

1 2 3 4 5   ▣ I sleep well at night. .... _____

1 2 3 4 5   ▣ I have regular physical checkups. .... _____

1 2 3 4 5   ▣ I often have indigestion. .... _____

1 2 3 4 5   ▣ I often eat fast. .... _____

1 2 3 4 5   ▣ I often eat at fast-food restaurants. .... _____

1 2 3 4 5   ▣ I tire easily. .... _____

1 2 3 4 5   ▣ I understand it takes good physical health to achieve other goals in life. .... _____

1 2 3 4 5   ▣ I am frequently sick. .... _____

1 2 3 4 5   ▣ I often experience tension in my family or social life. .... _____

1 2 3 4 5   ▣ I am in better physical shape than the average person my age. .... _____

1 2 3 4 5   ▣ I always fasten my seat belt. .... _____

1 2 3 4 5   ▣ I usually follow rules of safety. .... _____

1 2 3 4 5   ▣ I have made a conscious effort to reduce sodium, fat, and sugar in my diet. .... _____

☼ **Go back and review your ratings, one at a time. In the right hand column, put a + if you are pleased with your rating, or put a − if you would like to improve the area described.**

Source: Life Skills for Teens: Reproducible Masters for Middle and High School Students, by S. Palomares and D. Schilling, 1994, Austin, TX: PRO-ED. Copyright 1994 by PRO-ED, Inc. Adapted with permission

Name _____   Date _____

Health Quiz

☀ **Circle your answer (Yes or No) to each question.**
Then put a ✓ in the box next to the questions you want to learn more about.

☐ **1.** Do I know what to do if I am sick or hurt? . . . . **Yes**   **No**

☐ **2.** Do I know what to do if there is an emergency? . . . . **Yes**   **No**

☐ **3.** Do I know how to get Medicare/Medicaid or other health insurance? . . . . **Yes**   **No**

☐ **4.** Do I understand how to use Medicare/Medicaid or other health insurance? . . . . **Yes**   **No**

☐ **5.** Do I know how to find a doctor? . . . . **Yes**   **No**

☐ **6.** Do I know how to find a dentist? . . . . **Yes**   **No**

☐ **7.** Do I know how to find a counselor? . . . . **Yes**   **No**

☐ **8.** Do I know how to call and make my own appointments? . . . . **Yes**   **No**

☐ **9.** Do I know how to use any medication that I take? . . . . **Yes**   **No**

☐ **10.** Do I know how to get my medication filled? . . . . **Yes**   **No**

☐ **11.** Do I know what I need to know about sex? . . . . **Yes**   **No**

☐ **12.** Do I know what I need to know about drugs and alcohol? . . . . **Yes**   **No**

☐ **13.** Do I know where to find help if someone I know has a problem with drugs or alcohol? . . . . **Yes**   **No**

☐ **14.** Do I try to exercise? Do I have a plan to stay in shape? . . . . **Yes**   **No**

Source: Adapted and used with permission of Julie Haffner.

Name _____   Date _____

Health and Wellness Skills

1. Describe any special medical needs you have.

_____

2. Name your doctor and dentist.

_____

3. Can you select and make regular appointments with your doctor and dentist?

_____

4. Identify persons or agencies that can help you with medical and dental health problems.

_____

5. Describe how you organize and keep health records (e.g., immunization, medical, dental).

_____

6. Identify ways to avoid/prevent health problems, diseases, or injuries.

_____

7. Can you administer basic first aid?

_____

8. Describe what to do in case of emergency.

_____

9. Can you read and follow medicine labels and instructions?

_____

10. Describe how you store and take medicine properly.

_____

11. What regular cardiovascular exercise do you engage in?

_____

12. What regular strength and flexibility exercise do you engage in?

_____

13. How do you monitor your heart and breathing rate?

_____

14. How do you maintain appropriate weight?

_____

Source: The Self-Advocacy Strategy: Transition Skills Lists (p. 165), by A. K. Van Reusen, C. S. Bos, J. B. Schumaker, and D. D. Deshler, 1994, Lawrence KS: Edge Enterprises. Copyright 1994 by Van Reusen, Bos, Schumaker, and Deshler. Adapted with permission.

15. How do you select and eat nutritious foods?

_____

16. How do you prepare and store foods correctly to avoid bacteria and illness?

_____

17. How do you avoid exposure to harmful substances including cigarette smoke, pollution, drugs, and alcohol?

_____

18. How do you observe safety precautions (e.g., wearing seat belts, not drinking and driving, wearing appropriate clothing for weather)?

_____

19. How do you plan for relaxation/quiet time for yourself?

_____

20. How do you say "no" if already overburdened?

_____

21. How do you monitor your blood pressure and cholesterol levels?

_____

22. How do you take care of common illnesses: colds, flu?

_____

23. How do you warm up before and cool down after exercising?

_____

24. How do you practice safe sexual behavior?

_____

25. How do you use relaxation techniques?

_____

Source: The Self-Advocacy Strategy: Transition Skills Lists (p. 165), by A. K. Van Reusen, C. S. Bos, J. B. Schumaker, and D. D. Deshler, 1994, Lawrence KS: Edge Enterprises. Copyright 1994 by Van Reusen, Bos, Schumaker, and Deschler. Adapted with permission.

Being Sexually Active

☀ **Put a check mark in the Agree or Disagree column to show how you feel about each statement. Add your comments below each statement.**

Agree   Disagree

❏   ❏   **1.** If our relationship is based totally on sex, there is no relationship.

_____

❏   ❏   **2.** If a boy tells me that I have to have sex with him to show him that I love him, it's a signal right there. I will not have anyone put that kind of rule on me.

_____

❏   ❏   **3.** If you really love someone, like enough to think about marrying him or her someday, sex is okay.

_____

❏   ❏   **4.** Sex is okay as long as you practice "safe sex." As long as you use a condom, you'll be okay.

_____

❏   ❏   **5.** There's nothing wrong with virginity.

_____

❏   ❏   **6.** Teenagers today have to think about getting AIDS and HIV. We have to be more responsible than our parents were at our age.

_____

❏   ❏   **7.** Most kids don't have sex until they are about 17. That's old enough to make responsible decisions.

_____

❏   ❏   **8.** After my boyfriend and I had sex, he seemed to lose interest in me. I felt like I had been used. That hurt more than anything else.

_____

❏   ❏   **9.** I know of several kids my age who have already had babies. I don't want to have to deal with that. I want to stay young, stay a kid, and have fun for as long as I can.

_____

❏   ❏   **10.** It's not a big deal to say you chose to abstain from sex. It's becoming more and more accepted. It's a good thing.

_____

❏   ❏   **11.** Having premarital sex is totally against my religion. I just don't believe it is morally right.

_____

❏   ❏   **12.** If it feels good, do it.

_____

Source: Life Skills Activities for Secondary Students with Special Needs, by D. Mannix, 1995, West Nyack, NY: The Center for Applied Research in Education. Copyright 1995 by The Center for Applied Research in Education. Adapted with permission.

Name _____ Date _____

Rate the Risk

☼ **Rate the risk of each activity.**

HIGH	MEDIUM	LOW	
☐	☐	☐	**1.** Eating school lunches
☐	☐	☐	**2.** Taking your parent's car without asking
☐	☐	☐	**3.** Flying on an airplane
☐	☐	☐	**4**. Riding on a space shuttle flight
☐	☐	☐	**5.** Being in prison
☐	☐	☐	**6.** Walking down the hall at school
☐	☐	☐	**7.** Smoking cigarettes
☐	☐	☐	**8.** Calling someone who is bigger than you a nasty name
☐	☐	☐	**9.** Taking care of an unfamiliar dog
☐	☐	☐	**10.** Doing CPR on someone
☐	☐	☐	**11.** Cleaning a gun
☐	☐	☐	**12.** Landing an airplane in an emergency situation
☐	☐	☐	**13.** Riding a bicycle along a major street in your city
☐	☐	☐	**14.** Walking down a dark alley at night
☐	☐	☐	**15.** Burning leaves
☐	☐	☐	**16.** Taking cough drops
☐	☐	☐	**17.** Having surgery on your leg
☐	☐	☐	**18.** Having chemotherapy for cancer
☐	☐	☐	**19.** Rewiring the electricity in your house
☐	☐	☐	**20.** Driving on an icy road
☐	☐	☐	**21.** Having your ears pierced
☐	☐	☐	**22.** Driving drunk
☐	☐	☐	**23.** Driving while tired
☐	☐	☐	**24.** Going out with your best friend's steady date while the friend is out of town

Source: Life Skills Activities for Secondary Students with Special Needs (p. 513), by D. Mannix, 1995, West Nyack NY: The Center for Applied Research in Education. Copyright 1995 by The Center for Applied Research in Education.

Transportation & Mobility
List of Inventories

Name _____ Date _____

Transportation To and From Community Locations

☼ **Circle Y for yes or N for no under the appropriate column.**

	Student	Teacher	Parent
Travel Preparation			
Identifies current location	Y N	Y N	Y N
Identifies new location	Y N	Y N	Y N
Chooses from among transportation options	Y N	Y N	Y N
Obtains emergency phone numbers and places them in easily accessible place	Y N	Y N	Y N
Accesses and Uses Transportation			
Boards transportation	Y N	Y N	Y N
Lets driver know destination	Y N	Y N	Y N
Pays for travel	Y N	Y N	Y N
Follows personal safety rules	Y N	Y N	Y N
Demonstrates appropriate behavior	Y N	Y N	Y N
Reaches Destination			
Requests assistance for exiting transportation	Y N	Y N	Y N
Exits transportation	Y N	Y N	Y N
Moves to destination	Y N	Y N	Y N
Spends Time at Location			
Initiates activity at new location	Y N	Y N	Y N
Ceases activity at appropriate time	Y N	Y N	Y N
Returns From Location			
Moves to transportation vehicle	Y N	Y N	Y N
Boards transportation	Y N	Y N	Y N
Lets driver know location of destination	Y N	Y N	Y N
Pays for travel	Y N	Y N	Y N
Requests assistance for exiting transportation	Y N	Y N	Y N
Exits transportation	Y N	Y N	Y N
Moves to destination	Y N	Y N	Y N

Source: Functional Assessment and Curriculum for Teaching Everyday Routines: Secondary (pp. 64–65), by J. R. Arick, G. Nave, T. Hoffman, & D. A. Krug, 2004, Austin, TX: PRO-ED. Copyright 2004 by PRO-ED, Inc. Adapted with permission.

Name _____   Date _____

Functional Analysis of Transportation Behavior

☼ **Put a check mark in the box beside the behaviors the student demonstrates.**

Person completing the form: ❑ Student ❑ Parent ❑ Teacher

Walking to Places

☐ Use map to locate familiar places

☐ Follow street safety

☐ Use appropriate greetings

☐ Aware of stranger danger

☐ Not interrupt other people's business

☐ Aware of others' personal space

Arranging Public Transportation

☐ Use phone skills to make an appointment

☐ Know/find number

☐ Give introduction/greeting

☐ Request for need

☐ Know address going to and from

☐ Know what time to arrive

☐ Wait/listen for confirmation

☐ Initiate closure

☐ Respond to cue for closing confirmation

Using Public Transportation

☐ Be on time

☐ Have items ready before ride arrives

☐ Give quick greeting

Riding With Friends

☐ Be ready to leave a place when when it is time

☐ Always wear seat belt

☐ Be courteous

☐ Avoid touching gadgets in car

☐ Ask before touching radio, window, air conditioning, etc.

☐ Help with directions to familiar places

☐ Do not give directions if the person does not need them

☐ Get out right, within reasonable time

☐ Keep all belongings together in the car

☐ Remove all belongings from car

☐ Transition easily to new activities

☐ Show bus pass

☐ Sit down quickly

☐ Ride without making commotion

☐ Say a short goodbye

☐ Exit quickly at stop

Source: The Community Transition Program, by S. Keete (www.transitioncoalition.org). Adapted with permission.

Name _____ Date _____

Getting Around Town

☀ **Circle your answer (Yes or No) to each question.**
Then put a ✓ in the box next to the questions you want to learn more about.

❑   **1.** Do I know my way around town? . . . .   **Yes**   **No**

❑   **2.** Do I know how to read a map and follow directions? . . . .   **Yes**   **No**

❑   **3.** Do I know the transportation choices I can use in my city to get from place to place? .   **Yes**   **No**

❑   **4.** Do I know what I need to know about using the bus? . . . .   **Yes**   **No**

❑   **5.** Do I know what I need to know about using a taxi? . . . .   **Yes**   **No**

❑   **6.** Do I know what I need to know about driving a car? . . . .   **Yes**   **No**

❑   **7.** Do I know how to get a driver's license? . . . .   **Yes**   **No**

❑   **8.** Do I know what I need to know about car insurance? . . . .   **Yes**   **No**

❑   **9.** Do I know where to get my car fixed if it breaks down? . . . .   **Yes**   **No**

❑ **10.** Do I understand what I have to do to keep a car running? . . . .   **Yes**   **No**

❑ **11.** Do I know what I need to know about basic traffic laws? . . . .   **Yes**   **No**

❑ **12.** Do I know what the symbols on street signs mean? . . . .   **Yes**   **No**

❑ **13.** Do I know someone who can give me a ride if I need one? . . . .   **Yes**   **No**

Source: Adapted and used with permission of Julie Haffner.

Name _____ Date _____

Round-Trip Assessment

Destination _____ **Evaluator** _____

☀ **Rate the student's skill.**

	Yes	Assistance Needed	Not Applicable	Comments
1. Wears appropriate clothing	❑	❑	❑	_____
2. Locates bus stop accurately	❑	❑	❑	_____
3. Locates rail stop accurately	❑	❑	❑	_____
4. Boards correct bus	❑	❑	❑	_____
5. Boards correct train	❑	❑	❑	_____
6. Pays fare correctly	❑	❑	❑	_____
7. Obtains needed transfer tickets	❑	❑	❑	_____
8. Exits bus at correct stop	❑	❑	❑	_____
9. Exits train at correct stop	❑	❑	❑	_____
10. Notifies driver of needed stop	❑	❑	❑	_____
11. Asks driver for needed directions	❑	❑	❑	_____
12. Boards and exits bus independently	❑	❑	❑	_____
13. Boards and exits train independently	❑	❑	❑	_____
14. Uses special seating for individuals with disabilities	❑	❑	❑	_____
15. Allows enough time to catch bus or train on return trip	❑	❑	❑	_____

Source: Community Living Skills Workbook for the Head Injured Adult, by D. K. Angle and J. M. Buxton, 1991, Austin, TX: PRO-ED. Copyright 1991 by PRO-ED, Inc. Adapted with permission.

Name _____ Date _____

Driving Habits

1. How do you prefer to get around?

   ❏ Drive myself

   ❏ Have someone drive me

   ❏ Use public transportation or a taxi

2. When is the last time you drove? *(month and year)*

   _____

3. In an average week, how many days per week do you normally drive?

   _____ days per week.

4. During the past year, have you driven in your immediate neighborhood?

   ❏ Yes   ❏ No

5. During the past year, have you driven to places beyond your neighborhood?

   ❏ Yes   ❏ No

6. During the past year, have you driven to neighboring towns?

   ❏ Yes   ❏ No

7. During the past year, have you driven to distant towns?

   ❏ Yes   ❏ No

8. During the past year, have you driven to places outside of the country?

   ❏ Yes   ❏ No

9. During the past year, have you driven to places outside this region?

   ❏ Yes   ❏ No

10. Do you wear glasses or contact lenses when you drive?

    ❏ Yes   ❏ No

11. Do you wear a seat belt when you drive?

    ❏ Always   ❏ Sometimes   ❏ Never

12. How would you rate the quality of your driving?

    ❏ Excellent   ❏ Good   ❏ Average   ❏ Fair   ❏ Poor

13. How fast do you usually drive compared to the general flow of traffic?

    ❏ Much faster   ❏ Somewhat faster

    ❏ About the same

    ❏ Somewhat slower   ❏ Much slower

14. If you had to go somewhere and didn't want to drive yourself, what would you do?

    ❏ Ask a friend or relative to drive me

    ❏ Call a taxi or take the bus

    ❏ Use a community transportation service

    ❏ Drive myself regardless of how I feel

    ❏ Cancel or postpone the plan and stay home

    ❏ Other _____

15. During the past 3 months, have you driven when it was raining?

    ❏ Yes   ❏ No

16. During the past 3 months, have you made left-hand turns across oncoming traffic?

    ❏ Yes   ❏ No

17. During the past 3 months, have you driven on interstates, highways, or expressways?

    ❏ Yes   ❏ No

18. During the past 3 months, have you driven on busy roads?

    ❏ Yes   ❏ No

Source: Driver Rehabilitation: A Guide for Assessment and Intervention, by W. Stav, 2004, San Antonio, TX: Harcourt Assessment. Copyright 2004 by Harcourt Assessment, Inc. Adapted with permission.

19. During the past 3 months, have you driven in rush-hour traffic?

❑ Yes   ❑ No

20. During the past 3 months, have you driven at night?

❑ Yes   ❑ No

21. How many crashes have you been involved in over the past year when you were the driver?

_____

22. How many times in the past year have you been pulled over by the police, regardless of whether you received a ticket?

_____

23. How many times in the past year have you received a traffic ticket (other than a parking ticket) where you were found guilty, regardless of whether or not you think you were at fault?

_____

If there are any concerns about your driving habits, explain how you will address them. _____

_____

_____

_____

~~~~~~

☀ **Consider all the places you drive in a typical week, and fill in the information below to calculate the total miles you drive per week.**

Place	Number of Trips a Week		Miles from Home and Back		Total Miles
Store	_____	×	_____	=	_____
Church	_____	×	_____	=	_____
Work/Volunteer	_____	×	_____	=	_____
Relative's house	_____	×	_____	=	_____
Friend's house	_____	×	_____	=	_____
Out to eat	_____	×	_____	=	_____
Appointments (doctor, dentist, etc.)	_____	×	_____	=	_____
Other _____	_____	×	_____	=	_____

Total Miles per Week   _____

Source: Driver Rehabilitation: A Guide for Assessment and Intervention, by W. Stav, 2004, San Antonio, TX: Harcourt Assessment. Copyright 2004 by Harcourt Assessment, Inc. Adapted with permission.

Name _____   Date _____

Drinking and Driving

☀ **Circle Agree or Disagree to show how you feel about each statement.**

1. You should never drink alcohol and then drive. . . . .   **Agree**   **Disagree**

2. You should never ride in a car with someone who drinks and drives. . . . .   **Agree**   **Disagree**

3. Drinking and driving is the leading cause of death for teens. . . . .   **Agree**   **Disagree**

4. If most of my close friends were drinking at a party and then one offered to drive home, I
   would drink too, even if I knew I would ride home with one of them. . . . .   **Agree**   **Disagree**

5. It is embarrassing to call your parents to come pick you up at a party. . . . .   **Agree**   **Disagree**

6. I know of someone who was killed or injured in a drunk-driving accident. . . . .   **Agree**   **Disagree**

7. My parents don't care if I drink as long as I don't drive. . . . .   **Agree**   **Disagree**

8. I would stop drinking if I had a close call with a drunk driver. . . . .   **Agree**   **Disagree**

9. I am familiar with the alcohol education taught in health class or other programs as it
   relates to drinking. . . . .   **Agree**   **Disagree**

10. If adults brought in wrecked cars from drunk-driving accidents, students would laugh. . . . .   **Agree**   **Disagree**

Source: Life Skills Activities for Secondary Students with Special Needs (p. 277), by D. Mannix, 1995, West Nyack, NY: The Center for Applied Research in Education. Copyright 1995 by The Center for Applied Research in Education. Adapted with permission.

Leisure

List of Inventories

Recreation and Leisure Activities

1 List at least three things that you do in your free time.

_____

_____

_____

2 List three of your favorite activities or games.

_____

_____

_____

3 List three activities you and your family do together in your free time.

_____

_____

_____

4 List three of your favorite outdoor activities.

_____

_____

_____

5 List any clubs or groups you belong to.

_____

_____

_____

6 List three of your favorite records or musicians.

_____

_____

_____

Source: Functional Living Skills for Moderately and Severely Handicapped Individuals (p. 63), by P. Wehman, A. Renzaglia, and P. Bates, 1985, Austin, TX: PRO-ED. Copyright 1985 by PRO-ED, Inc. Adapted with permission.

Name _____   Date _____

Home Functional Skill Assessment

Person completing the form: ☐ **Student** ☐ **Parent** ☐ **Teacher**

Social/Leisure

	YES	WITH SUPPORT	NO
Identifies leisure activities	☐	☐	☐
Identifies resources for leisure activities	☐	☐	☐
Plans a leisure time event	☐	☐	☐
Engages in simple fine motor activities	☐	☐	☐
Operates electronic entertainment equipment	☐	☐	☐
Engages in craft activities	☐	☐	☐
Goes bowling	☐	☐	☐
Goes swimming	☐	☐	☐
Participates in Special Olympics	☐	☐	☐
Engages in track and field activities	☐	☐	☐
Has a hobby	☐	☐	☐
Reads for entertainment	☐	☐	☐
Develops meaningful relationships	☐	☐	☐
Recognizes rules of privacy of neighbors	☐	☐	☐
Uses a calendar to plan activities	☐	☐	☐
Visits with neighbors	☐	☐	☐
Walks for exercise	☐	☐	☐

Sexuality

	YES	WITH SUPPORT	NO
Understands aspects of relationships	☐	☐	☐
Knows appropriate time/place for masturbation	☐	☐	☐
Understands appropriate sexual behavior in community	☐	☐	☐

Source: *Career/Transition Planning Forms,* by Area Education Agency 4, n.d., Sioux Center, IA: Author. Copyright by Area Education Agency 4. Adapted with permission.

Leisure Activities

☀ **Put a ✓ in the box beside the things you like to do.**

Home

❑ Play records

❑ Play CDs

❑ Play computer games

❑ Listen to the radio

❑ Play board games

❑ Play lawn games

❑ Shoot pool

❑ Work puzzles

❑ Watch TV/videos

❑ Read newspapers/books/magazines

❑ Complete art projects

❑ Complete woodwork projects

❑ Build a collection

❑ Exercise

❑ Use exercise equipment

❑ Care for a pet (_____)

❑ Garden

❑ Write stories

❑ Keep a journal

❑ Keep a photo album

❑ Other _____

School

❑ Attend skill-building class

❑ Play team sports

❑ Participate as a team member/manager

❑ Use the school library

❑ Participate in extracurricular activities (e.g., clubs)

❑ "Hang-out" with peers

❑ Attend school functions (e.g., sporting events, plays, dances, etc.)

❑ Other _____

Community

❑ Walk/jog

❑ Ride bike/motorcycle

❑ Skateboard/Rollerblade

❑ Swim

❑ Golf

❑ Ski

❑ Go to video arcade

❑ Fish

❑ Operate a model plane/car

❑ Ride horses

❑ Participate with youth groups

❑ Participate in church activities

❑ Attend community events

❑ Use the public library

❑ Attend movies

❑ Bowl

❑ Eat out

❑ Attend concerts

❑ Participate in lessons/camps

❑ Attend family parties

❑ Attend arts/crafts class

❑ Other _____

Source: The School and Community Integration Project Curriculum for Students with Severe Disabilities, 1992, Salt Lake City: University of Utah, Department of Special Education, The School and Community Integration Project. Copyright 1992 by The School and Community Integration Project, Department of Special Education, University of Utah. Adapted with permission.

Name _____   Date _____

Parent Leisure Activities Survey

Survey completed by _____

1. What are your child's favorite leisure activities?

_____   _____

_____   _____

2. List some indoor *or* outdoor activities your family enjoys doing together.

_____   _____

_____   _____

3. List special space or transportation needs to be considered in planning leisure or recreation activities for your child.

_____   _____

_____   _____

4. Are there other people at home who spend leisure time with your child? What would you like your child to be able to do with these people?

_____   _____

_____   _____

5. Put check marks in the appropriate boxes for each activity listed.

	Activities That Interest My Child	Activities Available at Home	Activities Not Available at Home
Stereo	❑	❑	❑
Computer games	❑	❑	❑
Age-appropriate books	❑	❑	❑
Television	❑	❑	❑
Board games	❑	❑	❑
Basketball hoop	❑	❑	❑
Computers	❑	❑	❑
Radio	❑	❑	❑
Other _____	❑	❑	❑
Other _____	❑	❑	❑
Other _____	❑	❑	❑

Source: Functional Living Skills for Moderately and Severely Handicapped Individuals (p. 62), by P. Wehman, A. Renzaglia, and P. Bates, 1985, Austin, TX: PRO-ED. Copyright 1985 by PRO-ED, Inc. Adapted with permission.

Name _____ Date _____

Hobby and Interest Inventory

☀ **Which hobbies do you enjoy? Mark an X in the spaces that match your interests.**

	I Really Enjoy	I Would Like To Improve	I Would Like To Try
1. Individual sports (tennis, swimming) .	_____	_____	_____
2. Team sports (basketball, soccer) . . .	_____	_____	_____
3. Games (Monopoly, cards, checkers). .	_____	_____	_____
4. Reading.	_____	_____	_____
5. Cooking.	_____	_____	_____
6. Visiting friends	_____	_____	_____
7. Talking on the phone	_____	_____	_____
8. Walking.	_____	_____	_____
9. Sewing	_____	_____	_____
10. Attending school	_____	_____	_____
11. Working on cars	_____	_____	_____
12. Working on bicycles	_____	_____	_____
13. Roller-skating.	_____	_____	_____
14. Ice-skating.	_____	_____	_____
15. Doing carpentry.	_____	_____	_____
16. Model building	_____	_____	_____
17. Acting	_____	_____	_____
18. Playing a musical instrument	_____	_____	_____
19. Singing	_____	_____	_____
20. Watching television	_____	_____	_____
21. Listening to music	_____	_____	_____
22. Writing poetry	_____	_____	_____
23. Fishing	_____	_____	_____
24. Baby-sitting	_____	_____	_____
25. Drawing pictures	_____	_____	_____
26. Furniture refinishing	_____	_____	_____
27. Lifting weights	_____	_____	_____
28. Stamp collecting	_____	_____	_____
29. Working with animals.	_____	_____	_____

Source: *Hobby Inventory* by Project Bicep, Barnstable Public Schools, n.d.

	I Really Enjoy	I Would Like To Improve	I Would Like To Try
30. Photography	_____	_____	_____
31. Working with electronics	_____	_____	_____
32. Collecting things	_____	_____	_____
33. Participating in clubs	_____	_____	_____
34. Sailing	_____	_____	_____
35. Camping	_____	_____	_____
36. Sight-seeing	_____	_____	_____
37. Hiking	_____	_____	_____
38. Rock hunting	_____	_____	_____
39. Beachcombing	_____	_____	_____
40. Studying animals	_____	_____	_____
41. Doing experiments	_____	_____	_____
42. Working on word puzzles	_____	_____	_____
43. Doing gymnastics	_____	_____	_____
44. Doing research	_____	_____	_____
45. Decorating	_____	_____	_____
46. Bowling	_____	_____	_____
47. Arts and crafts	_____	_____	_____
48. Thinking	_____	_____	_____
49. Writing stories	_____	_____	_____
50. Gardening	_____	_____	_____
51. Exploring	_____	_____	_____
52. Kite flying	_____	_____	_____
53. Writing letters to friends	_____	_____	_____
54. Working with computers	_____	_____	_____
55. Working outdoors	_____	_____	_____
56. Working with older people	_____	_____	_____

Source: Hobby Inventory by Project Bicep, Barnstable Public Schools, n.d.

Name _____   Date _____

Musical Experiences

Yes, I can do this.	I need support to do this.	
		Music Listening at Home
☐	☐	**1.** Acquire music-listening equipment (e.g., radios, CD players, iPod)
		• Budget for equipment
		• Locate equipment for purchase
☐	☐	**2.** Use music listening equipment
		• Manipulate equipment (e.g., turn equipment on and off and control volume)
		• Maintain equipment (e.g., clean and store)
		• Avoid injury while using equipment (e.g., demonstrate appropriate procedures for plugging power source to equipment)
☐	☐	**3.** Access music via musical programs on television and radio
		• Find music program listings in printed guides
		• Access channels like MTV, etc.
		Social Behaviors at Dances
☐	☐	**1.** Locate and access dance lessons
☐	☐	**2.** Ask a person to dance
☐	☐	**3.** Deal with rejection
		Community Music Group Participation
☐	☐	**1.** Locate and access music lessons
☐	☐	**2.** Locate and access community music groups
☐	☐	**3.** Behave appropriately during rehearsals and performances

Source: It's Music to My Ears, by G. Buck and M. A. Gregoire, 1996, *Teaching Exceptional Children, 29*(1), pp. 45, 47. Reston, VA: The Council for Exceptional Children. Copyright 1996 by The Council for Exceptional Children. Adapted with permission.

Yes, I can do this.	I need support to do this.	
		## Accessing Concerts
☐	☐	**1.** Locate information about concerts
		• Find and read the community calendar section in newspapers
☐	☐	**2.** Purchase concert tickets
		• Budget for concert
		• Locate ticket purchasing center
		• Purchase ticket
☐	☐	**3.** Access transportation to and from concerts
		• Identify location of a concert
		• Determine available modes of transportation
		• Budget for transportation
		• Access transportation
		## Social Behaviors During Concerts
☐	☐	**1.** Dress appropriately
☐	☐	**2.** Know when and when not to talk during a concert
☐	☐	**3.** Access public restrooms
☐	☐	**4.** Know when and when not to applaud
☐	☐	**5.** Discriminate among types of concerts and expected behaviors in each type (e.g., rock vs. classical concerts)

Source: It's Music to My Ears, by G. Buck and M. A. Gregoire, 1996, *Teaching Exceptional Children, 29*(1), pp. 45, 47. Reston, VA: The Council for Exceptional Children. Copyright 1996 by The Council for Exceptional Children. Adapted with permission.

Name _____   Date _____

Functional Analysis of Leisure Behavior

Person completing the form: ❑ **Student**   ❑ **Parent**   ❑ **Teacher**

	Can Do		
Public Entertainment	**Independently**	**Partially**	**Not At All**
1. Call friend to schedule	❑	❑	❑
2. Make a date	❑	❑	❑
3. Put appointments in date book	❑	❑	❑
4. Be on time for transportation	❑	❑	❑
5. Act appropriately	❑	❑	❑
6. Thank friends for a good time	❑	❑	❑
7. Make sure has the correct amount of money for activity	❑	❑	❑

Visiting a Sit-Down Restaurant			
1. Wait for seat if necessary	❑	❑	❑
2. Locate desired item on menu	❑	❑	❑
3. Place order	❑	❑	❑
4. Wait patiently for food	❑	❑	❑
5. Eat with manners	❑	❑	❑
6. Sit casually after dining	❑	❑	❑
7. Read check	❑	❑	❑
8. Pay check	❑	❑	❑
9. Leave tip	❑	❑	❑
10. Use communication strategies/sequences	❑	❑	❑
11. Use augmentative device for clarification when necessary	❑	❑	❑

Going to a Movie			
1. Choose a movie	❑	❑	❑
2. Buy ticket	❑	❑	❑
3. Buy food at concessions	❑	❑	❑
4. Find correct theater	❑	❑	❑
5. Find seat without being disruptive to others	❑	❑	❑
6. Sit quietly through movie	❑	❑	❑
7. Locate public restrooms	❑	❑	❑
8. Use communications strategies/sequences	❑	❑	❑
9. Use augmentative device for clarification when necessary	❑	❑	❑

Source: The Community Transition Program, by S. Keete (www.transitioncoalition.org). Adapted with permission.

Recreation Facilities	Can Do		
	Independently	Partially	Not At All
1. Wait patiently for assistance	❑	❑	❑
2. Ask to borrow equipment	❑	❑	❑
3. Sign checkout sheet	❑	❑	❑
4. Change clothes in appropriate area	❑	❑	❑
5. Use locker for storage	❑	❑	❑
6. Use exercise equipment	❑	❑	❑
7. Interact with other patrons	❑	❑	❑
8. Return equipment to check-in counter	❑	❑	❑
9. Follow rules	❑	❑	❑
10. Use communication strategies/sequences	❑	❑	❑
11. Use augmentative device for clarification when necessary	❑	❑	❑

Video Store or Library

	Independently	Partially	Not At All
1. Take necessary materials	❑	❑	❑
2. Browse quietly	❑	❑	❑
3. Locate movie or book	❑	❑	❑
4. Ask for help	❑	❑	❑
5. Request specific movie or book	❑	❑	❑
6. Rent movie or check out book or movie	❑	❑	❑
7. Note due dates in planner	❑	❑	❑
8. Use communication strategies/sequences	❑	❑	❑
9. Use augmentative device for clarification when necessary	❑	❑	❑

"Downtime" at Home With Roommates

	Independently	Partially	Not At All
1. Lock and unlock door	❑	❑	❑
2. Able to share items	❑	❑	❑
3. Able to initiate activities with peers	❑	❑	❑
4. Able to make phone calls to friends	❑	❑	❑
• Ask for correct person	❑	❑	❑
• Identify self by using first name	❑	❑	❑
• Ask if the person is busy	❑	❑	❑
• Respond appropriately if person is busy	❑	❑	❑
• Present subject to discuss	❑	❑	❑
• Initiate casual conversation	❑	❑	❑
• Follow a one-topic conversation to completion	❑	❑	❑
• Answer questions asked	❑	❑	❑
• Make appropriate requests	❑	❑	❑

Source: The Community Transition Program, by S. Keete (www.transitioncoalition.org). Adapted with permission.

	Can Do		
	Independently	Partially	Not At All
• Make thorough plans	❏	❏	❏
• Communicate about common interests or what other person is interested in	❏	❏	❏
• Initiate closing to conversation.	❏	❏	❏
• Respond quickly to others' closing	❏	❏	❏
• Say good-bye once	❏	❏	❏
• Leave appropriate message with phone number on voice mail	❏	❏	❏
5. Give roommates personal space	❏	❏	❏
6. Listen to music/watch TV/play video games	❏	❏	❏
• Know acceptable volume.	❏	❏	❏
• Check to see if roommate is studying, sleeping, talking on phone, listening to music already, etc.	❏	❏	❏
• Check to see if roommate is "not in the mood"	❏	❏	❏
• Negotiate and decide with partner what music will be played . .	❏	❏	❏
7. Negotiation skills.	❏	❏	❏
8. Handle conflict between roommates.	❏	❏	❏
9. Use self-advocacy skills when needed	❏	❏	❏
10. Pick up subtle cues from roommates	❏	❏	❏
11. Give people space and privacy.	❏	❏	❏
12. Avoid going into others' bedrooms if they are not at home	❏	❏	❏
13. Knock on doors before entering.	❏	❏	❏
14. Use appropriate levels of touching	❏	❏	❏
15. Avoid interrupting if another person is involved in an activity	❏	❏	❏
16. Ask before entering someone's bedroom	❏	❏	❏
17. Answer knock on the door.	❏	❏	❏
• Find out who is there before unlocking the door.	❏	❏	❏
• Open door only to a person known	❏	❏	❏
• Know how to respond if the person is not known	❏	❏	❏
• Use appropriate social skills if the person is not known	❏	❏	❏
18. Answer phone calls for self and others	❏	❏	❏
19. Take messages for roommates	❏	❏	❏
20. Deal with telemarketers	❏	❏	❏

Source: *The Community Transition Program,* by S. Keete (www.transitioncoalition.org). Adapted with permission.

Community Participation
List of Inventories

Name _____   Date _____

Activities for Adult Outcomes in the Community

☼ Please rate the importance of each instructional activity for the student's future by circling the appropriate number. These activities may be used to develop instructional objectives on the IEP.

Person completing the form _____

1 = Consider for this year   **2 = In progress**   **3 = Addressed and completed**

1	2	3	Become aware of community interests and options
1	2	3	Develop shopping skills
1	2	3	Learn to order and dine at restaurants
1	2	3	Develop skills to ensure personal safety
1	2	3	Assess vulnerability status
1	2	3	Learn to use public transportation
1	2	3	Obtain a driver's license
1	2	3	Obtain a state identification card
1	2	3	Open and learn to use a bank account
1	2	3	Learn to schedule appointments
1	2	3	Become aware of rights regarding physical accessibility
1	2	3	Identify and check eligibility requirements for adult support
1	2	3	Register for military selective service
1	2	3	Register to vote, and learn to to vote at local precinct
1	2	3	Explore guardianship issues
1	2	3	Other _____
1	2	3	Other _____

List other skills needed by the student in this area.

_____

_____

_____

Name _____ Date _____

Community Functional Skill Assessment

☀ **Put a check mark in the column that matches the student's skill level.**

Person completing the form: ❑ **Student** ❑ **Parent** ❑ **Teacher**

Resources

	YES	WITH SUPPORT	NO
1. Identifies leisure activities	❑	❑	❑
2. Identifies public restrooms	❑	❑	❑
3. States telephone number	❑	❑	❑
4. Dials operator for assistance	❑	❑	❑
5. Obtains numbers through directory assistance	❑	❑	❑
6. Dials written telephone numbers	❑	❑	❑
7. Dials telephone numbers presented orally	❑	❑	❑
8. Obtains telephone assistance in an emergency	❑	❑	❑
9. Finds numbers in a telephone directory	❑	❑	❑
10. Places long-distance calls	❑	❑	❑
11. States consequences of breaking vs. obeying law	❑	❑	❑
12. Uses 911 properly	❑	❑	❑

Mobility

	YES	WITH SUPPORT	NO
1. States address	❑	❑	❑
2. Identifies modes of transportation	❑	❑	❑
3. Reads street signs and addresses	❑	❑	❑
4. Obeys traffic signals and signs	❑	❑	❑
5. Discriminates right from left	❑	❑	❑
6. Arrives at neighborhood destination by following instructions	❑	❑	❑
7. Gives directions from work to home	❑	❑	❑
8. Plans departure in order to arrive on time	❑	❑	❑
9. Crosses street safely	❑	❑	❑
10. Behaves appropriately in public	❑	❑	❑

Source: Career/Transition Planning Forms, by Area Education Agency 4, n.d., Sioux Center, IA: Author. Copyright by Area Education Agency 4. Adapted with permission.

Community Independence

	YES	WITH SUPPORT	NO
1. Uses bank	☐	☐	☐
2. Uses library	☐	☐	☐
3. Uses post office	☐	☐	☐
4. Goes to theater	☐	☐	☐
5. Goes to parks	☐	☐	☐
6. Orders at fast food restaurant	☐	☐	☐
7. Orders at restaurant	☐	☐	☐
8. Pays for own purchase at restaurant	☐	☐	☐
9. Operates vending machine	☐	☐	☐
10. Pays bills on time	☐	☐	☐
11. Cashes paycheck	☐	☐	☐
12. Carries money appropriately	☐	☐	☐
13. Tells time to nearest			
• Hour	☐	☐	☐
• Half hour	☐	☐	☐
• Quarter hour	☐	☐	☐
• 5 min.	☐	☐	☐
14. Shops at grocery store for 1–3 items	☐	☐	☐
15. Shops at dollar store for 1–3 items	☐	☐	☐
16. Shops at pharmacy for 1–3 items	☐	☐	☐

Government

	YES	WITH SUPPORT	NO
1. Recognizes need for			
• Fire department	☐	☐	☐
• Ambulance	☐	☐	☐
• Police	☐	☐	☐
2. Recognizes community services			
• Post office	☐	☐	☐
• Hospital	☐	☐	☐
• Police station	☐	☐	☐
• Fire station	☐	☐	☐
• Church	☐	☐	☐
3. Understands concept of rules and laws	☐	☐	☐

Source: Career/Transition Planning Forms, by Area Education Agency 4, n.d., Sioux Center, IA: Author. Copyright by Area Education Agency 4. Adapted with permission.

Name _____ Date _____

Adult Supports and Services

☀ **Circle your answer (Yes or No) to each question.**
Then put a ✓ in the box next to the questions you want to learn more about.

❑ **1.** Do I know what supports and services I get now? . . . .　**Yes**　　**No**

❑ **2.** Do I know what I need to start doing now to get the supports and services
　　that can help me live the life I want to live? . . . .　**Yes**　　**No**

❑ **3.** Do I know someone that I trust to help me find the supports and services
　　I can get after high school? . . . .　**Yes**　　**No**

❑ **4.** Do I know what programs and services are in my community that I
　　might be able to use? . . . .　**Yes**　　**No**

❑ **5.** Do I know about Rehabilitation Services? . . . .　**Yes**　　**No**

❑ **6.** Do I know about Social Security? . . . .　**Yes**　　**No**

❑ **7.** Do I know about Medicare/Medicaid? . . . .　**Yes**　　**No**

❑ **8.** Do I know about money that may be out there to help me live
　　and work on my own? . . . .　**Yes**　　**No**

❑ **9.** Do I know where to find out more about adult supports and services? . . . . . .　**Yes**　　**No**

Source: Adapted and used with permission of Julie Haffner.

Name _____   Date _____

Community Involvement Skills

☀ Put a ✓ in the box next to the skills you can do, and list examples in the space to the right of each skill.

I Can
Do This

❏　**1.** Locate and use the nearest shopping center _____

❏　**2.** Locate and use local public and private transportation _____

❏　**3.** Locate and use local and state employment services and agencies _____

❏　**4.** Locate and use local, state, federal, and professional service organizations _____

❏　**5.** Locate and use local or state counseling and guidance services _____

❏　**6.** Contact local emergency services _____

❏　**7.** Locate and use family and children's services _____

❏　**8.** Locate and select child-care services _____

❏　**9.** Locate and use vocational training institutions and programs _____

❏　**10.** Locate and use state agencies for individuals with special needs _____

❏　**11.** Locate and use housing agencies _____

❏　**12.** Locate and use the emergency room at the nearest hospital _____

❏　**13.** Locate and use health services _____

❏　**14.** Locate and use the postal services and other mail services _____

❏　**15.** Locate and use the library _____

❏　**16.** Identify sources of information about community events and activities _____

❏　**17.** Register and vote _____

❏　**18.** Read or listen to the news _____

❏　**19.** Participate in political functions, if interested _____

❏　**20.** Participate in civic clubs and organizations _____

❏　**21.** Participate in religious organizations, if interested _____

❏　**22.** Volunteer in an area of interest _____

Source: The Self-Advocacy Strategy: Transition Skills Lists (pp. 164, 168), by A. K. Van Reusen, C. S. Bos, J. B. Schumaker, and D. D. Deshler, 1994, Lawrence KS: Edge Enterprises. Copyright 1994 by Van Reusen, Bos, Schumaker, and Deshler. Adapted with permission.

Name _____   Date _____

Citizenship and Legal Skills

☀ **Read each skill and put a check mark in the column that best describes your ability.**

	No	With Help	Yes
1. Respect and obey laws and the Constitution of the United States	❏	❏	❏
2. Respect the rights and property of others	❏	❏	❏
3. Acquire information about important community and national issues	❏	❏	❏
4. Promote the belief in equality of opportunity for all people	❏	❏	❏
5. Respect individual differences and ways of life that are different from your own	❏	❏	❏
6. Use natural resources wisely	❏	❏	❏
7. Take an active part in government (e.g., voting, volunteering, serving on juries)	❏	❏	❏
8. Complete a voter registration application	❏	❏	❏
9. Participate in political parties	❏	❏	❏
10. Explain why citizens are required to pay taxes (e.g., income, sales, Social Security)	❏	❏	❏
11. Apply for licenses and permits (e.g., driver's, hunting, fishing, marriage)	❏	❏	❏
12. File a petition or complaint	❏	❏	❏
13. Contact persons or agencies that can assist you with legal problems	❏	❏	❏
14. Interpret contracts and agreements	❏	❏	❏
15. Organize, store, and retrieve important legal documents	❏	❏	❏
16. State your civil and constitutional rights	❏	❏	❏
17. State your rights as mandated under IDEA	❏	❏	❏
18. State your rights as mandated under Section 504 of the Rehabilitation Act	❏	❏	❏
19. State your rights as mandated under the Americans with Disabilities Act	❏	❏	❏
20. Advocate for yourself	❏	❏	❏

Source: The Self-Advocacy Strategy: Transition Skills Lists (pp. 164, 168), by A. K. Van Reusen, C. S. Bos, J. B. Schumaker, and D. D. Deshler, 1994, Lawrence KS: Edge Enterprises. Copyright 1994 by Van Reusen, Bos, Schumaker, and Deshler. Adapted with permission.

Name _____ Date _____

Functional Skill Assessment

☀ **Put a check mark in the column that matches the student's skill level.**

Person completing the form: ❑ Student ❑ Parent ❑ Teacher

	Strong	Acceptable	Weak	No Way To Tell	Not Applicable

Mobility

	Strong	Acceptable	Weak	No Way To Tell	Not Applicable
State my address	___	___	___	___	___
State my own telephone number	___	___	___	___	___
Identify modes of transportation	___	___	___	___	___
Read street signs/addresses	___	___	___	___	___
Obey traffic signals/signs	___	___	___	___	___
Discriminate right from left	___	___	___	___	___
Arrive at a neighborhood destination by following directions	___	___	___	___	___
Give directions from work to home	___	___	___	___	___
Arrive at a destination using map	___	___	___	___	___
Locate office by number	___	___	___	___	___
Locate building by street number	___	___	___	___	___
Plan departure in order to arrive on time	___	___	___	___	___
Obtain street address from telephone directory	___	___	___	___	___
Obtain driver's license	___	___	___	___	___
Travel downtown	___	___	___	___	___
Ride bicycle	___	___	___	___	___
Drive car	___	___	___	___	___
Wear safety belt in vehicle	___	___	___	___	___
Locate designated areas within facility	___	___	___	___	___

Community Independence

	Strong	Acceptable	Weak	No Way To Tell	Not Applicable
Use library	___	___	___	___	___
Use post office	___	___	___	___	___
Go to the theater	___	___	___	___	___
Go to parks	___	___	___	___	___

➲

Source: Career/Transition Planning Forms, by Area Education Agency 4, n.d., Sioux Center, IA: Author. Copyright by Area Education Agency 4. Adapted with permission.

	Strong	Acceptable	Weak	No Way To Tell	Not Applicable
Order meals in a cafeteria	_____	_____	_____	_____	_____
Order at fast food restaurants	_____	_____	_____	_____	_____
Order at a restaurant	_____	_____	_____	_____	_____
Pay for my own purchase at a restaurant	_____	_____	_____	_____	_____
Pay to next highest dollar	_____	_____	_____	_____	_____
Operate vending machines	_____	_____	_____	_____	_____
Operate a savings account	_____	_____	_____	_____	_____
Operate a checking account	_____	_____	_____	_____	_____
Pay bills on time	_____	_____	_____	_____	_____
Cash my paycheck	_____	_____	_____	_____	_____
Tell time to the nearest:					
• Hour	_____	_____	_____	_____	_____
• Half hour	_____	_____	_____	_____	_____
• Quarter hour	_____	_____	_____	_____	_____
• 5 min	_____	_____	_____	_____	_____

Social and Leisure

	Strong	Acceptable	Weak	No Way To Tell	Not Applicable
Identify leisure times and activities	_____	_____	_____	_____	_____
Identify resources for leisure activities	_____	_____	_____	_____	_____
Plan a leisure time event	_____	_____	_____	_____	_____
Engage in table games (dominoes, cards, board games)	_____	_____	_____	_____	_____
Join a club/organization	_____	_____	_____	_____	_____
Listen to music	_____	_____	_____	_____	_____
Watch TV	_____	_____	_____	_____	_____
Operate electronic entertainment equipment	_____	_____	_____	_____	_____
Engage in craft activities	_____	_____	_____	_____	_____
Go bowling	_____	_____	_____	_____	_____
Go swimming	_____	_____	_____	_____	_____
Play soccer	_____	_____	_____	_____	_____
Play softball	_____	_____	_____	_____	_____
Participate in Special Olympics	_____	_____	_____	_____	_____
Engage in track/field activities	_____	_____	_____	_____	_____
Put puzzles together	_____	_____	_____	_____	_____
Engage in simple gross motor activities (swinging, jumping, walking, dancing)	_____	_____	_____	_____	_____

Source: *Career/Transition Planning Forms,* by Area Education Agency 4, n.d., Sioux Center, IA: Author. Copyright by Area Education Agency 4. Adapted with permission.

	Strong	Acceptable	Weak	No Way To Tell	Not Applicable
Participate in a hobby	_____	_____	_____	_____	_____
Read for entertainment	_____	_____	_____	_____	_____
Play an instrument	_____	_____	_____	_____	_____
Develop meaningful friendships	_____	_____	_____	_____	_____
Recognize rules of privacy of neighbors	_____	_____	_____	_____	_____
Uses a calendar to plan activities	_____	_____	_____	_____	_____

Sexuality

Recognize need for privacy	_____	_____	_____	_____	_____
Understand aspects of relationships	_____	_____	_____	_____	_____
State aspects of sexual anatomy	_____	_____	_____	_____	_____
Use appropriate birth control	_____	_____	_____	_____	_____
Demonstrate knowledge of sexually transmitted diseases	_____	_____	_____	_____	_____
Decide the appropriate time and place for masturbation	_____	_____	_____	_____	_____
Understand appropriate sexual behavior in community	_____	_____	_____	_____	_____

Services

Recognize need for	_____	_____	_____	_____	_____
• Fire department	_____	_____	_____	_____	_____
• EMS	_____	_____	_____	_____	_____
• Police	_____	_____	_____	_____	_____
Recognize community services	_____	_____	_____	_____	_____
• Hospital	_____	_____	_____	_____	_____
• Police Station	_____	_____	_____	_____	_____
• Fire Station	_____	_____	_____	_____	_____
• School	_____	_____	_____	_____	_____
• Church	_____	_____	_____	_____	_____
Understand concept of rules and laws	_____	_____	_____	_____	_____
State consequences of breaking vs. obeying law	_____	_____	_____	_____	_____

General Skills

State my full name	_____	_____	_____	_____	_____
Understand greater than, less than, and equal to	_____	_____	_____	_____	_____
Use calculator	_____	_____	_____	_____	_____

Source: *Career/Transition Planning Forms*, by Area Education Agency 4, n.d., Sioux Center, IA: Author. Copyright by Area Education Agency 4. Adapted with permission.

	Strong	Acceptable	Weak	No Way To Tell	Not Applicable
Identify equivalents	_____	_____	_____	_____	_____
Identify coins	_____	_____	_____	_____	_____
Count change	_____	_____	_____	_____	_____
Budget money	_____	_____	_____	_____	_____
Write checks	_____	_____	_____	_____	_____
Balance a checkbook	_____	_____	_____	_____	_____
Use banking services	_____	_____	_____	_____	_____
Use vending machines	_____	_____	_____	_____	_____
Tell time	_____	_____	_____	_____	_____
Read calendars	_____	_____	_____	_____	_____
Schedule events by time	_____	_____	_____	_____	_____
Get information from pictures and packages	_____	_____	_____	_____	_____
Read survival words/signs	_____	_____	_____	_____	_____
Demonstrate understanding of reading context	_____	_____	_____	_____	_____
Read books	_____	_____	_____	_____	_____
Alphabetize	_____	_____	_____	_____	_____
Spell common words	_____	_____	_____	_____	_____
Write letters	_____	_____	_____	_____	_____
Use dictionary for spelling, if necessary	_____	_____	_____	_____	_____
Dial programmed phone	_____	_____	_____	_____	_____
Place long-distance calls	_____	_____	_____	_____	_____

Source: *Career/Transition Planning Forms,* by Area Education Agency 4, n.d., Sioux Center, IA: Author. Copyright by Area Education Agency 4. Adapted with permission.

My Community

☼ **Circle your answer (Yes or No) to each question.**
Then put a ✓ in the box next to the questions you want to learn more about.

❑   **1.** Do I know how I can get involved in my community? . . . .   **Yes**   **No**

❑   **2.** Do I know who I can talk to in my community if I have questions or need help? . . . .   **Yes**   **No**

❑   **3.** Do I want to do volunteer work? . . . .   **Yes**   **No**

❑   **4.** Do I know where I can volunteer? . . . .   **Yes**   **No**

❑   **5.** Do I know how to find a nearby grocery store? . . . .   **Yes**   **No**

❑   **6.** Do I know how to find a nearby mall? . . . .   **Yes**   **No**

❑   **7.** Do I know how to find a nearby Wal-Mart or Target? . . . .   **Yes**   **No**

❑   **9.** Do I know how to find a nearby laundromat? . . . .   **Yes**   **No**

❑   **10.** Do I know how to find a nearby post office? . . . .   **Yes**   **No**

❑   **11.** Do I know how to find a nearby place of worship (if that is important to me)? . . . .   **Yes**   **No**

❑   **12.** Do I know how to find a nearby recreation center, YMCA, or athletic center? . . . .   **Yes**   **No**

❑   **13.** Do I know how to find a nearby hospital? . . . .   **Yes**   **No**

❑   **14.** Do I know how to find a nearby doctor's office? . . . .   **Yes**   **No**

❑   **15.** Do I know how to find a nearby dentist's office? . . . .   **Yes**   **No**

❑   **16.** Do I know how to find a nearby pharmacy? . . . .   **Yes**   **No**

❑   **17.** Do I know how to find a nearby public library? . . . .   **Yes**   **No**

❑   **18.** Do I know how to find a nearby bus stop? . . . .   **Yes**   **No**

❑   **19.** Do I know how to find a nearby airport? . . . .   **Yes**   **No**

Source: Adapted and used with permission of Julie Haffner.

Name _____   Date _____

Community Resources

☀ You probably use a lot of different community resources and don't even think about it.
Write a place that would be a community resource for each activity listed.

If I wanted to . . .

◾ Borrow a book to read, I would go to _____

◾ Fly to another state, I would go to _____

◾ Catch a bus to the mall, I would go to _____

◾ Buy a CD, I would go to _____

◾ Work with people who were sick, I would go to _____

◾ Play softball, I would go to _____

◾ Get some exercise, I would go to _____

◾ Get my teeth cleaned, I would go to _____

◾ See a doctor, I would go to _____

◾ Cash my pay check, I would go to _____

◾ Mail a letter, I would go to _____

◾ Pay a traffic ticket, I would go to _____

◾ Get a marriage license, I would go to _____

◾ Apply for Social Security, I would go to _____

◾ Apply for admission to a college, I would go to _____

Source: Whose Future Is It Anyway?, by M. Wehmeyer and K. Kelchner, 1995, Arlington, TX: The Arc. Copyright 1995 by The Arc. Adapted with permission.

About the Authors

☀ **Katherine O. Synatschk,** PhD, LPC, is the executive editor at PRO-ED and an adjunct professor at Texas State University. She has been the director of counseling for a large urban school district, a high school counselor, a school social worker, a special education teacher, and a counselor educator. She trains and consults on counseling issues at the local, state, national, and international levels. Her writing and research interests include using solution-focused counseling approaches to help children and adolescents achieve goals, implementation of accountability in school counseling programs, and transition and career planning for all students.

☀ **Gary M. Clark,** EdD, is a professor of special education at the University of Kansas. His professional interest in adolescents with disabilities goes back to his work as a teacher, school counselor, and vocational rehabilitation counselor in Texas. He has contributed to the state transition guidelines for Kansas and Utah and has been a consultant in a number of states for career development, transition programming, life skills curricula, transition assessment, and secondary special education teacher education. Dr. Clark has authored numerous books, chapters, and tests in the area of transition planning.

☀ **James R. Patton,** EdD, is currently an independent consultant and adjunct associate professor in the Department of Special Education at the University of Texas at Austin. He formerly was a special education teacher, having taught students with special needs at the elementary, secondary, and postsecondary levels of schooling. He has written books, chapters, articles, and tests in the area of special education. Dr. Patton's current areas of professional interest are the assessment of the transition strengths and needs of students, the infusion of real-life content into existing curricula, study skills instruction, behavioral intervention planning, and the accommodation of students with special needs in inclusive settings. He is also working as a mental retardation forensic specialist in regard to death-penalty cases in Texas and throughout the country.